THE PILATES OF GEBLIK

Jack Fitzsimons

Kells Publishing Co Ltd
John Street
Kells
Co Meath
Ireland

Contact: kellspublishing@gmail.com

First published 2016

ISBN 978-1-872490-57-1

*Dedicated with love and gratitude
to my wonderful wife, Anne.*

*A portrayal of rustic life in a part of Ireland
in the twentieth century,
a period of unprecedented change,
of innocence, intrigue and horror,
told with candour in intimate
and sometimes disturbing detail.*

*Each chapter, while an integral part of the narrative,
is presented as a story in itself.*

When sorrows come, they come not single spies but in battalions.
William Shakespeare, *Hamlet*

CONTENTS

PREFACE

In June 2009, I underwent treatment for cancer in the Mater Private Hospital. I was not long out of intensive care when a friend visited me. He was accompanied by an impressive young entrepreneur to whom I gave the first four chapters of this book. It seemed most unlikely that I would be able to add any more. He contacted me soon afterwards, stating that this was a book waiting to be published and, when completed, he would do that for me. He added: *"It is such a powerful story it needs to be told, please bring it to a conclusion."* No account could convey the sense of gratitude I owe to this gentleman so I will encapsulate my feelings with one simple but fervent word – thanks.

Jack Fitzsimons

New Curate Is A Holy Terror

Prologue

In the late 1920s, living conditions in the parish of Geblik were bad but had improved immeasurably from around one hundred years before. Clips from *Reports of the Irish Poor Law Commissioners* from that time (1836) and area give a flavour of the atrocious state of affairs:

Small one and two-room hovels often housed large families and animals. In one instance, not unusual, the father, mother and four children slept in one corner, a widow woman in the second, the donkey in a third, and the pig in a fourth, of a cabin about fourteen feet by twelve. Mention could be made of many similar cases among labourers, widows and aged persons of both sexes, whose two or three families lived in cabins of one room, and pigs, goats or cows lay in the other corners. The Archdeacon of Meath stated, at a public examination, that he had travelled all over Europe, but had never seen so miserable a peasantry in any country, and it was a perfect mystery to him how more than half of them managed to exist.

In consequence of the great increase of the population, of the strict enforcement by proprietors of agents of the law and the clauses in leases against the sub-division of land and the erection of new cabins, and the prevalence of the 'clearing system' (doing away with small holdings of land and pulling down cabins) within the past twenty years, the bogs had become complete villages. The labourer was to be found there in every gradation from comparative comfort (sic) to the lowest state of wretchedness.

The usual dimensions of cabins are: length, from 14 to 18 feet; width, 10 feet to 12; the side walls being from six to seven feet high. A few of them are built of rough stone, but almost all of them of mud. The interior is usually divided into two apartments by a cross wall of the same height of the side walls, but some only by mats or hurdles thatched with straw; many, however, of the poor cabins have only one apartment. The kitchen apartment is generally 10 or 12 feet square, the bedroom 10 or 12 feet by six or eight. Labourers' cabins never have a second storey, excepting one or two instances of a few cottages, built by resident proprietors for their own labourers; they have no ceiling but the roof. The thatch is usually of straw though some of the worst cabins are only thatched with potato stalks, reeds or rushes, or covered with sods. The thatching is frequently very bad and not water-tight, both from the thatch itself being rotten and worn out, and from the bending or breaking in of the rafters, which are often propped up in many places. The natural earth is the only floor, and it is only when the ground is so boggy as to be perpetually damp and soft, that a little clay is brought in to mix with and spread over it. The floor is very bad and uneven; it is also usually damp in winter, because in general considerably below the surface of the ground adjoining. This arises not only from the sod being cut off, but also often from some of the earth of which the walls are built being dug out of the very spot which afterwards forms the floor. In the bogs the Assistant Commissioners found cabins which had been built against banks, and the floor consequently formed of what had been formerly the bottom of a ditch; and some others were made by raising dwarf walls round pits dug three or four feet below the surface of the bog, from which turf had formerly been dug, so that these cabins were about half above and half below the ground, and *the floors, of course, excessively damp, especially in a soil naturally so wet and muddy. In spite of one of the driest and hottest summers ever known (the latter end of August), some of these floors were even then soft and spongy to the tread, notwithstanding which most of the inmates slept on the ground, with only a little straw or rushes under them.*

For a window these cabins seldom have anything but a small hole from 6 to 15 inches square, more generally about 9 or 10 inches square, which is stopped up with straw or an old bag, in bad weather. A window frame or glass is never met with but in a few cabins built by gentlemen or large farmers, for their own labourers. There are never any window shutters, and the only iron work in the cabin is the hooks upon which the doors are hung. They never have privies, and the majority have not even pigsties, for in most cases the pig sleeps before the fire, or is fastened up in a corner of the cabin. The cabins belonging to gentlemen and the larger farmers, usually occupied by their labourers, are generally also kept in better repair than formerly, and many of them have been improved of late years; but those belonging to little tradesmen and small occupiers, the repairs of which are generally thrown on the tenant, are as bad as ever, and remain the most wretched hovels which it is possible to conceive, without light or air, but what is derived from the door, filled with smoke which issues, as it happens, by the door, thatch, or hole in the roof, and generally by all three – damp, dark, dismal and unhealthy. These cabins would not in England be considered good enough to house cattle in.

The clothing of the labourers is very ragged and bad: men constantly employed generally buy a new coat only once in four or five years, if they have a large family: if a small one, once in two or three years. A man only occasionally employed is obliged to go two or three years longer without one, and some of them never get a new coat at all, but only cast-off clothes from their employers, or charitable persons. A man in constant employment cannot spare more than £1 or £1.10s in the year for clothes according to the size of his family; a labourer occasionally employed will spend from 10s to £1, according to his means and family. The man may get a pair of shoes for himself in the year, but the family must go barefooted, the children almost always. The use of shoes and stockings is not generally increasing except among the labouring men themselves, who are in some degree obliged to wear them to protect their feet in digging. The women often go barefooted, and the children, as just stated, almost always. The majority of women get their clothes made by others, most of them from ignorance, not knowing how to make them themselves, but many because they have not time themselves, from their numerous families, and some because they wish to have them more smartly made. The materials of the clothes of men or women are very seldom made at home. A very few make a little linen, and some a little course cloth, but, except knitting stockings, their home manufacturing has nearly disappeared.

Except in the more miserable cabins where the inmates all sleep on the ground, the parents, or master or mistress of the family, usually have a bedstead, or rather a frame of rough wood, split poles, or stout sticks, raised off the floor by stone blocks or other supporters. The children and rest of the family sleep on the floor. Even where a single man lives with his mother, sisters, aunts etc., he, as the master of the house, sleeps on the bedstead, and they on the floor. A second bedstead is very seldom to be found. The only bedding is straw, rushes, or, in a very few cases of unusual luxury, a course sacking tick filled with chaff. The more comfortable labourers have a piece of sacking or coarse calico, or bale-cover, over the straw, by way of under sheet, but the poorer families have nothing. The covering consists of an old blanket, always very threadbare, and generally full of holes, and of pieces of old clothes, carpeting etc., patched together. In all cases the day-clothes of the family, especially the man's greatcoat, form the chief part of the night covering also; and in the poorer cabins they have nothing else, except a few rags and tatters, which scarcely hang together. Nothing can exceed the wretchedness met with in many of the cabins in this respect; a little damp dirty straw, or a few rushes, with a small bundle of rags for covering, are the only bed and bedding, in too many of the most desperate labourers' cabins, especially, for the children, or father, mother, brother, or sister of the man or his wife. In such cabins the inmates often pointed, in answer to the question of 'Where is your bed?' to a little heap in one of the corners of the cabin, which would in any other country have been readily taken (and not considered very good either in size or material) for the dog's bed, and which not infrequently differed very little in either the quantity or the quality of the bedding from that of the pig in the opposite corner. The greatest complaint, however, which the Assistant Commissioners heard, when visiting these wretched abodes, was the want of covering, not only from the cold in winter, but still more in wet weather, from the suffering caused by the necessity of covering themselves by night with the man's wet coat and other day-clothes, which for want of firing to dry them, and from the thickness of frieze coating, will remain wet, or exceedingly damp, for days afterwards.

The father, mother, and all the children, usually sleep together, until the eldest children are 10 or 12 years old. The latter are after that age put into a separate bed, and if they are of different sexes they sleep apart. If the cabin has two apartments the girls sleep in a bed in the room with their parents, and the boys in one made up in the kitchen; but if there is only one apartment in the cabin, the boys are put in a corner, and in some cases a sort of screen of mats, or of old clothes hung on a line, is put up at night in front of their bed. In the suburbs of towns and populous villages (where the greatest misery is always found) it is not unusual to find cabins containing only one room, in which a man, his wife, and four or five children, are sleeping in a bed at one end, or in one corner of the room, and one or two widows, or old men (either beggars, or persons assisted by their children who are at service), sleeping at the other end, or in opposite corners... The better kind of cabins have a little table, two or three stools, a chest or two for clothes, a dresser with a small number of plates, cups, and mugs, and a few pails, tubs, and pots and pans... seldom a dresser, and the stools, table, stock of crockery, and cooking utensils, are proportionally worse, and less numerous or almost nominal. As to chairs, drawers, and other furniture met with in English labourers' cottages, they were never heard of in the labourers' cabins here.

Among the instances of distress which the Assistant Commissioners met with in those bogs was one of a class very seldom found, considering the extent of population, and the state of the poor. It was a woman with an illegitimate child, of about four years old: as soon as the mother's pregnancy was discovered she was turned out by her brother, with whom she had lived since the father's death, and she had ever since been a houseless wanderer, without home or protection. She was ashamed to live near her native district, where her relatives and friends scouted her, and the very children hooted at her, and she maintained herself and child by knitting, and by the kindness of labourers' families, who took her in for a few days or a week or two at a time, charging her nothing for her lodging, but she was occasionally obliged to beg for her food. From the superior appearance and language of this unfortunate woman, the Assistant Commissioners suspected that she had been a comfortable farmer's daughter, and respectably brought up. She did all she could, short of direct falsehood, to make the Assistant Commissioners believe she was a widow, and they have no doubt that she passes for one wherever she is not known; but, there being no other person present, a little cross-questioning caused her to burst into tears, and to acknowledge the truth.

*

Ireland's woes and the terrible miseries of its people were in large part attributable to imperial Britain's annexation policy and confiscation of lands. This ruthless colonial subjugation was morally unjustifiable. But might was right and, as a result of the lust for power, countless people passed their lives in conditions unfit for animals.

On usurpation one of Britain's first acts was to build impressive, daunting courthouses and establish a police force and judiciary to enforce laws established on injustice and wrong. The armed police force, known as the Royal Irish Constabulary (RIC), and judges were recruited from the native Irish, as were the schoolteachers, grippers and all state jobholders, who were paid by Britain to do its iniquitous work. All of these collaborators had a stark choice to make: either get submerged with the doomed human dross or take the shilling to be well rewarded for giving the veneer of righteousness and respectability to what was – as the plight of the oppressed people demonstrated – intrinsically immoral and indefensible. Britain's investment in the bribery was repaid with interest, as the records show. RIC officers ruthlessly enforced the oppressive laws, interpreting them with despotic malice. One man, married with a large young family, got two months gaol when he was caught by a dutiful peeler poaching a pair of rabbits on ranch land. Another man, in similar family circumstances, over a long period saved up enough money to buy a pair of leather boots by poaching rabbits. When he was coming home from town, the new boots tied loosely together with whangs and thrown across his shoulder, he was apprehended by a vigilant RIC officer who demanded to know where he got the money to buy the boots. He was fortunate to be released without charge after several hours of rigorous questioning in Peter's Cross barracks. (In the history of Ireland's survival, the pre-eminent role of the humble rabbit has been usurped by the pig.)

The following report was published in *The Meath Chronicle* in 1905:

Liam Ua Siordain, of Oldcastle, has just been fined the sum of one shilling because his name was not painted in English on his cart. The law on the subject is that the name must be painted in 'legible' characters. Liam's name was painted quite legibly in Irish. The presiding magistrate was sympathetic, but the police swore that they could not read the name. This, we submit, only proves that the police are illiterate – it does not prove that the name is 'illegible'. Are Irishmen to be fined for using their own language simply because an illiterate bobby in the constabulary is unable to read it?

Two months later in the same paper:

It will be remembered that several persons in Ireland (including one in Meath, Liam Ua Siordain, of Oldcastle) have been prosecuted and fined of late for having their names in Irish on their carts, and the peelers acting in such cases have sworn that they are ignorant of the letters of the alphabet. Last week an order was sent out from the Inspector-General of Police to the effect that no prosecutions of this nature are to be made in future without authority from headquarters, which goes to prove that peelers who have already prosecuted did so solely and entirely under the pressure of their own mean anti-Irish prejudices.

The peelers, magistrates and all other colonial collaborators and lackeys sold their souls at the going rates and honoured the bargain scrupulously; they became more anti-Irish than the English themselves. Expediency became a dominant societal conditioner; religion, politics and morality were in thrall to circumstances. Many priests had chosen the religious way of life for pragmatic reasons – some of them had not the height requirement for the police or failed in competitive examinations for entry to the banks or other prestigious institutions. The same consideration applied to women joining religious orders; such a vocation was a respectable fall-back for superior ladies who were surplus to appropriate communal demands. This mundane social dimension was a critical, if not the only significant, factor in subliminal canonically rigged conditioning and covert motivation.

The fight for land never ceased and seemed to be making tolerable headway. In 1919, an estate in the parish of Geblik, consisting of over five-hundred acres, passed to the tenants and landless men of the district. There were twenty-three allotments, including a cow park, and because of the large number of applicants the selections were made by ballot. But due to penury the reality was that many of those who acquired divisions were no better off – and maybe worse because they lost out on benefits such as the right to employment with the local authority. It was reported in *The Meath Chronicle* that the draw was conducted in a manner that gave entire satisfaction to all concerned – this could be because many of the losers considered themselves the lucky ones!

Britain's role in Irish affairs was not totally negative, however. Despite its abysmal failure to avert or cope with the calamity of the Great Famine, for example, workhouses had been built all over the country in the nineteenth century and these despised and degrading institutions saved many lives. Health services

21

Jack Fitzsimons

were developed and expanded, agrarian reforms brought rays of hope, limited increases in incomes for agricultural produce gave an illusion of prosperity, railways and canals were built and minor industries established. But in its overall scheme of affairs depopulation of the countryside was in any event essential for the success of Britain's agenda; that was the rationale for the clearances. Britain sought to set up a model society of minions, and engineered deprivation, torture and death, with impunity, to achieve its purpose. The noble band of acclaimed patriots, and others whose deeds passed unnoticed, later to be reviled by asinine revisionists, made heroic sacrifices to achieve freedom because they knew that was the only way to justice and dignity. One of Britain's greatest crimes was to make monsters of countless Irishmen in order to shatter the yoke of serfdom and tyranny. The reprehensible dying kicks of the colonial monster were stifled with sacrifices, courage and bravery. So with the establishment of the Irish Free State Ireland neared the summit of an interminable road built by gallant martyrs. The sun shone warmly on the valley beyond. And Geblik, like every other place in that liberated realm, basked in the exhilarating kindling glow and savoured the exciting dawn of freedom.

*

The late 1920s was a period of progression and regression, of rise and fall, change and sameness. But old customs clung tenaciously, deep-rooted ingenuousness still flourished, the scourges of life remained largely unaffected.

Ceilidhing was the great social assuagement and conditioner, where implausible stories that reflected and shaped the ethos of a deprived nation were delivered by creative narrators to avid, gullible listeners.

22

"Did ye hear what happened to Larry Gibney? The fairies surrounded him in the Deerpark and only he got up on the big stone they'd have brought him with them! They tried every trick to get him down but he was too cute for them!"

"Tommy Murphy had a close one last week. Didn't he stray on to a fairy path when he was crossing the Lios field in broad daylight. He wasn't able to get out of it, a place that he knew like the back of his hand. After going around the field five or six times he turned his coat inside out and straight away got his bearing. But he's not the better of it yet."

"The ghost in Mackens is playing up again. Of all the ghosts in the parish – and there's a quare few of them around – this one is the father and mother of a villain! Even the fowl in the hen house can't settle with him, they can be heard squawking and panicking all through the night. They say there's a horrid holy missioner priest coming to try and settle him!"

"Siddy Kelly is yer only wan if ye lose something bad. Didn't Petey Malone lose the key of the mansion and his job was gone if he couldn't find it! He searched high up and low down but not a trace was to be found. Down he went to Siddy and she goes up to her room as usual taking a cup filled with some kind of a concoction. After about five minutes mumbling and grumbling she came down and gave him instructions: go to the front door of the Mansion and walk out forty paces, turn right for twenty paces and then right for ten. Petey did as he was instructed and brought Tom Hanley with him. It was getting dark at the time. 'Light a match until we take a look,' he says to Tom. 'What would I be lighting a match for,' Tom replied, 'isn't the key there at yer toe!'"

End of Prologue

New Curate Is A Holy Terror

The priest has always been a revered figure in Ireland. Reasons for this are historical and social as well as religious. But undoubtedly the greatest reason would centre on the role and aspirations of the priesthood – to honour God by serving others. Greater love than this no man hath.

Priests in the main were well-rounded characters who went about their work in a dedicated and often heroic manner despite serious obstacles and difficulties. Drafted from the better-off sections of society they had leadership qualities and vocational commitment to varying degrees; many were gifted in particular ways, some had personal difficulties, others had conspicuous traits or idiosyncrasies. Those characteristics were significant not only in the day-to-day running of a parish but in its development as well.

Within a very short space of time on duty following a clerical appointment all the notable facets of an incumbent's make-up would be discerned, considered and analysed by parishioners. The essence and disposition of a new priest was infallibly determined in much the same way as a farmer would evaluate an animal at the fair; the spontaneous assessment by the farmer might lack the clinical endorsement of a rigorous examination under a veterinary professional but it would be no less perspicacious and effectual. A new priest's significance as a factor in parochial concerns would be arbitrarily considered by worshippers at first exposure on the altar and a firm view generally established before the day ended. While such a seemingly perfunctory appraisal might be considered illogical and prone to error it is debatable if a thorough pathological assessment by an expert could be more profound or revealing. In most cases, however, priests fitted comfortably into their roles and a common view evolved over time. But in instances where behaviour did not accord with the norm a more urgent situation prevailed and branding within a couple of weeks would be effectuated. The aptitude for weighing up character accurately to the nearest gram was an accomplished pastoral diversion.

*

A new priest always brought a palpable buzz to any parish. Various trace elements could be identified in such a perturbation – simple and natural aversion to change, apprehension, indolence, sadness, maybe, and old-fashioned curiosity would be high on the list. Most excitement related to a parish priest but a new curate also caused considerable ripples. Generally, a parish priest was appointed for life, whereas curates, for unknown reasons (although there were often guesses and talk), seldom got time to establish strong roots in the one place. In any event, when it was announced in the spring of 1926 that the Rev. Peter Glennon was to be transferred as curate to the parish of Geblik, rumours spread in the region that he was a very tough, exacting character of rare zeal, and mixed feelings of unease and trepidation permeated nearly every household in the area. Fr Joseph Drake, a fairly mundane character, was administrator, acting for the parish priest who had for some years been confined to a mental institution.

People in the parish were bonded by many traits and circumstances – resilience and despair, deprivation, ignorance, sickness, courage and various social issues to different degrees. But the pervasive factor common to all was religion. It was the antidote to adversity, the stabiliser for imploding lives, the life buoy in a drowning sea. There was eternal hope in the Catholic Church founded by Christ and outside of which there was no salvation. The priest was the epitome of that conviction and could work miracles – lay ghosts, cure ills and do all kinds of incomprehensible things that became embodied in folklore. Didn't the parish priest of Tynalmoy, Fr Brogan, show up the Protestant minister when they both attended a tenants' rights meeting in Skell? The minister carefully hung his grand overcoat on a hook in the lobby on the way in, but Fr Brogan threw his frayed coat across a sunbeam! No one ever heard tell of a Protestant minister doing the like of that.

Geblik was a very small, nondescript rural parish outpost. It measured about seven miles north to south and an average of three and a half miles east to west. There were no outstanding or unusual features of any description within its boundaries. It had two Catholic churches, two national primary schools and one small village, Carnalstown, on the southern boundary. One of the schools was located here, along with two pubs, a post office and a former RIC barracks converted to a dwelling house with a small annex used as a huckster's shop. Two well-attended fairs were held annually. This hamlet was parodied in outside areas by unflattering verse: *Carnalstown of great renown has neither church nor steeple, but in every dure there stands a hoor gaping at the people!* Some peeved dignitary had allegedly referred to the parish as an arsehole of a place, which was rather harsh and unfair. True, like elsewhere, there was endemic poverty and vacuity, engendering noted characters who resorted persistently to wiles and roguery for survival and stimulation. Mischievous and disruptive elements were always on the prowl, particularly under cover of darkness. The odd malefactor could not be denied. There were few and limited social diversions or outlets. Class distinction was jealously and ruthlessly guarded. But, allowing for the unremitting adversity, and discounting a miscreant minority, it could be fairly claimed that no finer people graced any other area of Ireland.

In 1926, the population at Geblik was under one-thousand, with two-hundred-and-fifty households, of which six were non-Catholic families. There were five or six wealthy farmers who owned large tracts of land, others struggling hard to make ends meet, but the vast majority were landless workers in various stages of deprivation and poverty. According to knowledgeable people who consider such things, and as might be reasonably concluded (even allowing for the spiritual dimensions), Geblik was not a sought-after parish by any cleric; rather, it could be adopted as a rehabilitation station or a form of purgatory for recalcitrant or intractable priests. Such penitential arrangements were not confined to religious affairs either – in the neighbouring parish of Towncastle the Garda barracks of Peter's Cross (originally an RIC barracks erected to protect the plantation landlord) was sited in a remote and sparsely populated area at the edge of a bog. Until its closure in later years, many of the Gardaí stationed there had idiosyncratic traits that contravened the conventional notion of normality. There were, of course, others of distinction and great competence. These situations are not untypical.

Geblik, too, had experienced the exception that proves the rule. Rev. John Straws came as a curate there, on loan from another diocese, in 1913, and was transferred in 1915. But in that short space of time he brought about positive changes and gave a meaning to people's lives that would endure and be talked about in the parish for many years afterwards. He was a good and holy man, a born leader who, it was acknowledged, had his feet set firmly on the ground. Sodalities and devotions which he established always had full attendances. But he did not confine himself to the spiritual. His greatest aversion was to alcoholic drink, particularly overindulgence. He organised and trained a group of volunteers, using wooden guns for practice, to join in the fight for Irish freedom and justice. Despite his popularity, many mothers in the parish thanked God fervently that he was gone in 1916 or, they alleged, he would be the cause of having all their sons shot in the GPO during the Easter Rising!

The parish had, in fact, played its part during the Troubles. The mother of the leading patriot in 1916 came from parish stock. A sister of the lady that married Joseph Plunkett – who was the maid, the bride and the widow on the one day – had taught cookery and domestic economy to classes in the parish. A local man of limited intelligence had been executed by the IRA for associating with the Black and Tans. Sinn Féin courts had been held successfully. Independence brought pride and there was a stirring of hope.

Fr Straws loved the poor and had very little time for the wealthy. Classes in the Irish language, music and tradition thrived under his direction. Sinners and strugglers were especially welcomed, and all without exception revered and loved him. At the crowded farewell party held to mark his departure, in the parochial hall built in Carnalstown during his two-year stay, old and young cried bitter tears when he bid them a last goodbye. They knew they would never see his like again.

In the next eleven years, five curates came and went. Although, in the main, they performed their duties well, and did whatever curates have to do, none of them ever remotely possessed the gifts and the charms of Fr Straws. That was no reflection on them, however, because Fr Straws was unique and special. But with the appointment of every new curate afterwards there was a certain expectation, a hope that maybe someone particularly gifted would be appointed. That yearning helped to fuel the excitement of parishioners when the appointment of Fr Glennon was announced – was he assigned for his vice or his virtue?

*

Black Michael wasn't the cleverest of men, but he was crafty and cute as a pet fox. In parochial terms, he was a well-travelled man and spoke from experience and with conviction. But he had a propensity to exaggerate greatly at times and this, naturally, undermined his credibility. The hyperbole was nearly always self-evident.

"I remember lining out at centrefield in a football game with Meath in Jones' Road," he once told listeners, "and begod it was one of the best games I ever played. When I was returning to the dressing room after the game who comes through the crowds to shake hands with me but the bishop himself! 'You're the best fuckin' catch of a ball, Mick, that I ever saw,' says he to me."

For people who knew Black Michael, the bishop's language wasn't the biggest obstacle to credibility. He had never played with the local team – in fact, no one from the parish where he was born and reared ever saw him kick a ball in his life. He told eager listeners that he knew the new curate's family well and that he at one time had a romantic attachment to his sister.

"Well-off farmers," he claimed. "I used to do a week's threshing for them."

By occupation, Black Michael was a helper with a threshing mill and toured the country during the autumn and winter. He gave the impression that he drove the steam engine, a job that merited high social esteem, but in fact he never progressed beyond stoking the engine fires with coal, which caused him to be always black as soot and resulted in his nickname.

"He's a great wan," he said, referring to Fr Glennon. "Takes a drop of the cratur. And like the rest of them he's a cunt on courting! But by God can he preach! Can that man preach? He's as good as any missioner. There's them that claims he can do miracles as good as any saint."

Doubts arose regarding some aspects of these assertions. The romantic claim was scotched directly; it was reliably learned that Fr Glennon had only one sister, who was a nun. Besides, the general consensus was that Black Michael wouldn't know how to handle a woman if she threw herself at him, and he was never known to have such liaisons in all his forty or so years. Astute listeners concluded that he might have had notions of her in his imagination before she entered the convent. The wealth of the Glennon family was disputed too, although everyone was aware that priests only came from families with a comfortable and respectable background – they had to be a cut above the common. With the various stories circulating, and undergoing embellishments and mutations, a mood of concern and apprehension was created that reached fever point as the day for Fr Glennon's inception approached. For that brief space of time almost everything else in the parish was of minor significance.

*

It was a bright but cool Sunday morning as Fr Glennon emerged from the run-down, single-storey parochial house. He was setting out on his first assignment, to say mass in the chapel of ease at Holmogats, which was about a mile and a half distant. In appearance, he was about five foot, eight inches tall, stout with a reddish complexion, tight lips, receding hairline and severe, piercing eyes. Aged about forty-five years, dressed in black with heavy overcoat, hat and clipped trousers, his stiff upright posture on the big Raleigh bicycle conveyed an impression of incongruity, accentuated considerably as he leaned forward for extra leverage on the pedals over humps and hills. Until recently, priests had normally made this journey on horseback or by pony and trap.

Many of the older men, as well as some younger, were waiting as usual around the gateway until the priest turned the corner onto the main road, a couple of hundred yards distant. By the time he reached the church, not much more than a minute later, the majority of them had gone inside or were crowding to get in. The few hardy regulars, mostly elderly, remaining at the entrance, ceased puffing pipes and pulled at caps and hats to salute Fr Glennon as he dismounted at the gate. He acknowledged their greeting in an offhand, desultory way, raising his left hand and waving it slightly, giving the clear impression that he had more immediate and important matters on his mind. They watched him until he turned the corner to go into the vestry. When he had robed, a server pulled a rope five or six times in the outside belfry and, at the first tinny peel, the hard-boiled residue sauntered in to stand in an awkward, disparate bunch at the back of the cramped church.

The building was small and L-shaped with two pokey galleries and a tiny adjunct vestry to the rear. Arched windows and doors punctuated the thick pebble-dashed walls. A simple timber altar on a creaky platform, raised two steps against the back wall, was flanked by two windows with opaque glass. In one of these window openings there was a large plaster statue of St Joseph, and a matching statue of the Virgin Mary stared wistfully into the funereal interior from the other. A window outside the rickety timber altar rail housed a similar garish statue of a triumphant St Michael the Archangel with a spear, banishing to hell an abhorrent Lucifer enmeshed with poisonous and repulsive reptiles. High ceilings lined with wainscoting followed the slopes of the roof and the lower part of the walls was similarly finished to a height of about four feet. All the plastered walls were whitewashed. Lurid stations of the cross hung between windows. Narrow aisles were flanked with simple timber seats. There were two memorials on the walls of the long aisle to priests buried there; the inscription on one of these stated that the priest's family, in their great bereavement, took it on themselves to provide finances for the memorial, a claim that engendered dubiosity. At the end of the long aisle a framed memorial card invited prayers for the soul of Hanora Straws, the mother of the former beloved curate in the parish. In front of the altar the suspended oil lamp burned with a faint red glow while the lighted candles glimmered. Despite the drab setting, and the inconspicuousness of those attending, there was an electrifying feeling of expectancy that can only be generated by important occasions.

Mass proceeded in the normal respectful way without any particularly unusual occurrence. The gauche troupe of four gowned servers were as clumsy as usual and it was soon evident that Fr Glennon was rather sharp and impatient. He had a strong, clear voice with a slightly upper-class or affected ring to the incomprehensible Latin invocations. His movements were deferential but somewhat brusque or edgy. There was a coldness in the way he grimaced and a hardness in the large dark eyes. A small number received holy communion, then he removed the chasuble and traversed both aisles with a long-handled collection box, while a server collected the coppers on both galleries. After the collection he paused briefly in deep reflection, which helped him to catch his breath, then turned around on the altar to face the congregation and preach the sermon. This was the moment of truth for which everyone in the church had been waiting. The homily was the layman's barometer of a priest's worth; he was only as good as the sermon he could deliver.

There were no introductory words or gestures that might be considered appropriate for the occasion. Fr Glennon, with hands outstretched and held high, faced the people, without opening his mouth, for what seemed an eternity. He moved his eyes slowly around, scrutinising, penetrating the very soul of every individual in the church. Some shifted uneasily, others coughed or glanced sideways. Then the priest raised his two hands higher. The deadly silence and unbearable pause intensified the apprehension.

"Dearly beloved," he began. "I want to speak to you today on a very important part of the Gospel, what may be considered the most important part of the Gospel, the Crucifixion of Christ. We take the Crucifixion for granted, don't we? But without the Crucifixion there is no salvation. Do you understand what that means?"

He moved his eyes around the congregation in silence.

"Do you understand what it means?" he bellowed clearly, implying that they did not.

Then, after another long, uncomfortable pause, he answered,

softly and condescendingly, "it means there would be eternal damnation for every human being, hell for everyone and for all eternity. That's what it would mean if the Crucifixion had not taken place!"

He paused to take breath and lowered his hands, helping to drive the point home. Every member of the congregation viewed him with unease. Raising his arms, he continued.

"How many of you meditate on the Crucifixion of Christ?" he asked. "How many?"

Once more he looked slowly around the congregation, with everyone trying to avoid his stare. Nobody knew whether or not he expected an affirmation by a show of hands or nodding of heads.

"Maybe you don't know how to meditate as a Christian, to contemplate, to reflect. Let me help you then. Let me bring back to your minds what you were taught in the catechism. To meditate is to pray in a special way, to think for long over an event, with reverence and thanksgiving. We must think deeply because meditation involves the intellect, the one attribute that raises us humans above the animal level."

He paused again briefly for emphasis, then continued.

"To meditate on the Crucifixion we must know and understand the Gospel story. Before the act of Crucifixion, Christ was cruelly scourged, tied to a pillar. He was stripped naked and flogged with whips that had balls of lead at the ends of the leather lashes. The flogging continued until he was unable to stand, his body lacerated all over and covered in blood. Can you imagine the sight?" he roared. "Can you picture the torn flesh, the gushing blood?"

The discomfort of the congregation was palpable. Some moved sideways in their seats and fidgeted, others gazed at the floor or ceiling. A few closed their eyes. There were involuntary shakes and shivers. Feelings of nausea and fear registered on troubled brows of participants trapped before their tormentor in the stingy, congested church.

"Of course we blame the Roman soldiers, don't we? Oh, yes, we do! But who is really responsible for that cruel scourging?" he thundered. "Who must take the blame? Who?" he roared.

His eyes searched the captivated, unnerved audience like a powerful, controlled light beam. Suddenly he sprang around and pointed animatedly to the centre of the front pew.

"You!" he roared. "You, you, you," identifying Mary Julia Martin who, until then, had her eyes glued on him, mouth partly open in awe.

If the roof had collapsed it would have caused less consternation. Limbs went numb, hair stood on end, kidneys were pressurised. There were many members in the congregation who had endured hellfire admonitions before, generally by missionary preachers, but nobody had ever experienced such a traumatic, heart-wrenching and personalised sermon, and nobody was ready for it. To be picked out without warning as such an evildoer, in such a situation, was catastrophic.

"Oh, Jesus, Mary and Joseph," Mary Julia intoned fervently, swaying and grabbing for support, the residual blood draining from her already pale countenance, prayer book and rosary beads falling to the floor. Everyone leaned forward to get a glimpse of Christ's persecutor. A tall, attractive, mellowing, middle-aged spinster, at times detractively dubbed 'Last Rose of Summer', she had an influential role in parochial affairs. It was suspected she was one of a select coterie that had kept the priests well informed regarding any Catholics who failed to live up to their obligations, particularly where the shocking scandal of courting couples was an issue. Consequently, her extreme embarrassment brought considerable spontaneous pleasure to some members of the congregation who felt aggrieved for personal reasons.

But Mary Julia was a pillar of the church in the parish. With her bachelor brother she lived across the road from the chapel and was always available to help out with any chores. Nightly the rosary was recited in the house and any visitors ceilidhing there always joined in. Holy pictures adorned all the walls, a small red-globed oil lamp burned continuously in front of a picture of the Sacred Heart over the kitchen mantelpiece, and a mini altar with statues was well tended in the corner of her bedroom. She wore medals and read the *Messenger* from cover to cover. On a devotional level she recited prayers, in particular fixed numbers to certain saints, and was firmly of the opinion that through these intercessions she had brought an end to the World War, the Troubles, and the worldwide influenza epidemic, as well as many calamities of a lesser scale. In this respect she was no different to countless other good and sincere Catholic adherents. Generally, with some reservations, those positive attributes were recognised in the wider community. As a consequence, when Fr Glennon pointed the accusatory finger towards her, he was shaking the superstructure, if not the foundation, of religiosity in the place.

"The fuckin' Martins," Black Michael muttered at the back of the church. "I knew there was something bad about them. Never saw them put up a dacent male at a thrashin'! The curse o' god on the cunts!"

In a lower tone, Fr Glennon then included a few obviously less reprehensible culprits. "And you, and you, and you," he indicated, pointing randomly around. "Anyone who commits sin, particularly serious sin, is a conspirator in the scourging of Jesus. Don't let us fool ourselves by blaming the Roman soldiers."

Shaking with emotion, eyes bulging and perspiration rolling down his ruddy countenance, he had seemed to be on the point of an apoplectic fit until he abruptly calmed. Then he inched backwards and rested an elbow on the altar, all the time facing the congregation. For a time that seemed endless he stood there looking vacantly into space.

"Is he finished?" somebody asked in a frightened whisper, face covered with their hands, at the bottom of the long aisle.

"Is he what?" retorted Black Michael. "Begod, if I know anything, he hasn't rightly started yet!"

Again with hands outstretched and held shoulder high, Fr Glennon edged forward on the altar, his piercing, bulging eyes moving like searchlights probing every soul in the little church. The listeners were tense and apprehensive, many of them petrified. Mary Julia Martin continued to tremble but, with support from helping hands, managed to sit upright with some decorum.

"Yes, dearly beloved," he resumed, "Christ was whipped because of your sins. The ends of the thongs were fitted with balls of lead. Balls of lead, do you understand? Every stroke lacerated the flesh and drew spurts of blood. Any other human being would have died from the cruel flogging. And are you sorry or ashamed? No. No, you are not. Because if you were you would not continue to scourge Jesus with your sins."

Fr Glennon's manner of directing questions at the congregation was particularly intrusive and disconcerting, notwithstanding that, after nuanced pauses, he provided all the inimical answers.

"And when they had scourged him almost to death, what did they do? They matted a crown of thorns and squeezed it on his head! A matted coil of vicious barbs! You have never seen, nor can you imagine, such a contemptible and cruel crown. We are not talking of twisted briars like you see growing in the neglected ditches around the parish of Geblik, with sharp thorns maybe an inch long. These thorns in that reprehensible crown were like long sharp nails, they pierced and tore the flesh of Jesus as the wreath of shame and suffering was hammered cruelly on his head."

The tension was unbearable as the congregation agonised over the terrible pictures that were projected before the imagination. There were nervous coughs and glances and a seat creaked here and there. Some struggled against an urge to throw up or a feeling of faintness. Cold sweat exuded on troubled brows.

"We blame the Jews for that, don't we? Oh, yes, we take the coward's way out! But who is really to blame for that barbarous crowning with thorns? Who?" he roared.

His eyes again moved methodically, piercingly, around the church. Some people attempted to pray with their rosary beads, mouths dried, hearts pounded. Suddenly, he sprang sharply around and gesticulated frantically towards the middle of the long aisle.

"You," he yelled. "Yes, you, you!"

Those alongside the culprit moved away from him with alacrity, leaving Paddy Simons uncomfortably isolated. He was a small, balding labourer in his fifties, hard of hearing, and not quite sure about the implications of the unusual dramatics. He gaped inanely at his accuser, stroking the corners of his mouth stained with over-flowing tobacco spittle.

"The little hoor," Black Michael commented under his breath, "and he wouldn't be fit to keep the chaff from the mill! Blast him!"

Fr Glennon identified three or four other transgressors before again lapsing into silence and leaning backwards against the altar to settle the seething ardour. Finally, he resumed his position at the edge of the top step. As it was obvious he was embarking on another onslaught, the tension became almost unendurable.

"And now, my dearly beloved," he began, "we come to the final act of redemption, the most cruel act that could be perpetrated on a human being by other human beings, the Crucifixion. Let us contemplate, as we have never done before, the extreme suffering, the pain, the degradation and humiliation of Christ. Let us direct our thoughts to that supreme sacrifice made by Christ on the Hill of Calvary, nearly two-thousand years ago, in the hope that we may be inspired to make sacrifices for the saviour who died for us."

The congregation was typical of what would be encountered in any remote and impoverished rural parish. A front seat in the main gallery had a rug and was reserved for the biggest local landlord who was seldom in residence in the parish. Four or five families of consequence, wealthy farmers and an ex-RIC officer, with his family, sequestered foremost or favoured seats. But the main body of worshippers included many with patched and ragged clothes, the sick and hungry.

"Let us always try to be generous, not complain when we are asked to make small sacrifices in our lives," Fr Glennon entreated. "If the Crucifixion means anything to us it must inspire us in that way.

"Christ – Almighty God – was led like a lamb to the slaughter. On Calvary he was stripped naked and laid on a bare wooden cross. Then he was cruelly nailed to it with dreadful iron spikes before being raised on the hillside for all to mock and scorn. Can you imagine the pain, the agony, the humiliation? Picture yourself on that hillside, then. See the scourged Christ with the crown of thorns writhing on the cross in torment before you. What would you have done? What would you have done?" he thundered.

"For three hours Christ hung there, contorted with the most abominable suffering. No human mind can even begin to imagine the perversion, the mental and physical ravaging."

Suddenly, he calmed, exacerbating the sensation of unease and foreboding. Just as abruptly, he became animated again. The bloodshot eyes were distended, the face crimson, the lips pouted.

"And who was responsible for the Crucifixion?" he roared. "Who must take the blame? Who?" he persisted, the voice trembling, shifting, penetrative eyes striking terror into even the most intrepid souls. Then, in what appeared like divine revelation, he pointed animatedly towards the small group of hardened campaigners standing awkwardly at the end of the church.

"You," he bellowed, "you, you, you."

Everyone in the church turned around to note the degenerate. In the face of the unprecedented charge, the hitherto callous crust of the nonconformist bunch of hardy annuals collapsed. Some crouched low, others moved further back or to the sides, beyond the trajectory of the accusatory finger. Only one man held his place, at the front and in the centre. Jamesy Fitzhenry was positively amused at the development.

"Yes, you," Fr Glennon confirmed. "You with the hand in the pocket!"

For a compelling finale to his sermon, Fr Glennon had unfortunately picked the wrong man. Others might have been humiliated or embarrassed, some might even have felt the legs go from under them. But not Jamesy Fitzhenry. Although he was only in his mid-twenties, and enigmatic in many respects, he was tough as well as intelligent. A hardy, attractive farm labourer casually employed wherever work was available, his temperament was suspect; at times he could be calm and relaxed but, on other occasions, he might fly off the handle without warning. He was also one of the kind that in any crowd or predicament cannot avoid being pre-eminent and conspicuous. In this unprecedented situation he reacted with surprising equanimity. Conscious that all heads were turned in his direction, he shrugged and grinned bemusedly, then raised his right hand in a gesture of acknowledgement to Fr Glennon. Even those with little time for him could only admire the cool, almost insolent response to his accuser.

"The hoor of hell," murmured Black Michael. "The breed of him was bad! Could never be trusted! Wit' ye wan day and agin' ye the next!"

Fr Glennon waited until the congregation turned full concentration on him again. Then spreading his arms wide he spoke in a softer tone.

"My dearly beloved brethren, don't let us continue to take the easy way and blame Pontius Pilate for the Crucifixion. We must accept responsibility because of our sins. All of us share the blame, some more than others according to our wickedness. But to the extent that we repent and avoid serious sin, and the dangerous occasions of mortal sin, we reduce the sufferings of our saviour, Jesus Christ. In the name of the Father, and of the Son, and of the Holy Ghost, Amen."

He turned sharply in a spontaneous pivot towards the altar to don the chasuble and intone the final prayers. The severely traumatised and confounded congregation dropped to their knees, impelled more by a sensation of release and relief than by fervent supplication or veneration. Finally, Fr Glennon stridently led the *De Profundis* at the foot of the altar, genuflected reverently at its conclusion, then filed behind the gawky servers out of view behind the chipped, ochre-grained vestry door.

*

As usual after mass there was a stampede to get out of the church. The indecorous, unseemly crush might almost have taken the doors off the hinges. Then a crowd of the men congregated at the gates, putatively to discuss affairs, indifferent to the blocking of the passageway. (Black Michael claimed the prime intention was so that the women would have to squeeze through and rub up against them, the only opportunity some had for close encounters.) It was no different today, except that Mary Julia Martin was barely able to walk past the group, although stoutly supported by friends on both sides. There was psychological comfort for her, too, from caring women who felt blessed that they were not censured from the altar.

"Don't mind that priest, Mary Julia. Sure what does he know about you, not being a week in the parish. You never did nothing to nobody, so you didn't! And how many first Fridays did you make? God almighty! Blaming you for scourging Our Lord, and you wouldn't lift your finger to a child, so you wouldn't!"

"She'll be all right when she has a baby," someone suggested, meaning a baby Power whiskey.

Paddy Simons got a fair share of attention when he coalesced with the crowd at the gate. But, because of his deafness, events in the church had more or less passed over him. Nevertheless, he knew he was a player of some importance on the day, and the comments were not uncomplimentary.

"Begod, Paddy, you could have fooled me. I never knew it was in you! Where the hell did you come on the clipe o' thorns or how did you manage it at all at all?"

But the biggest acknowledgement was accorded to Jamesy Fitzhenry. He strutted around the excited group, hands in pockets, shoulders shrugging and eyes beaming. As somebody recalled afterwards, you'd think it was he that had saved humanity, not Christ. Or at least that he was an indispensable accomplice. Views expressed were generally personalised and predictable.

"Good man yerself, Pontius Pilate! The ould breedin' is there, son!"

"No bother to ye, Pontius, avick!"

"Did you wash yer hands in a dish this morning or was it in th'ould barrell?"

"Begod, Pontius, Christ wasn't the first unfortunate ye left hanging!"

"Nor won't be the last!"

Emergence of the servers around the corner of the church indicated that Fr Glennon was on his way out. The group fell into line along the wall, Jamesy Fitzhenry near the outer end. Except for the odd mutter of salutation there was complete silence as the priest passed by, sedately wheeling his bicycle, looking abstractedly into the distance. He acknowledged with a nod the multifarious gestures of reverence – hats and caps removed, pulled down or turned sideways, fingers to foreheads and obsequious gyrations. Some people would swear afterwards that he fixed a hard stare on Jamesy Fitzhenry as he passed, an understandable censure on a character that had subverted the sublime climax to his sermon. Moving to the centre of the road and placing his left foot on a purpose-built protrusion of the rear axle, he took a few hops before sliding into the saddle with surprising ease and poise. They watched him until he turned at the junction out of sight. Then the appraisals and verdicts were pooled.

"Bejaysus, he's wan hell of a priest," declared Micksheen the Blackguard. "The like of such a sermon was never heard. He'd put the heart crossways in any sinner!"

"Aye and them that never did no sin!" claimed Hughie the Thrush. "Who the hell would think it was in him?"

"He's what's long wanted in the parish. It's going to the dogs entirely, so it is. I'll tell ye something – he'll soon bring religion back to what it should be, so he will," asserted Butt Pat.

"Don't you know well that's why he was sent here!" interjected Larry McGovern.

"I'd say he has quare powers all right if it's put up to him", Joey the Prick McGinnity maintained. "But, begod, I wouldn't care to go to Confession to him! I saw wicked priests in me time, and the Redemptorists was the worst o' them be a mile. But he's the bedamnest case I ever met. There's rough times ahead if he's left here for long. A mission every five years is not too bad but would people be able for the like o' that every Sunday? An' how will he get on with Fr Drake? Will there be ructions in the parochial?"

Prick wasn't regarded as the most serious thinker, but he had a propensity for asking questions that were difficult to answer. He was so titled because families by the name of Stone lived on either side of him. Colloquially, his situation was described in male parlance as hanging out between a pair of Stones. Once, when he was forced by the Stone families to give evidence at court in a disputed trespass case, he complained to a baffled judge that he was dragged in that day by the Stones.

"If ye think that was a tough sermon," declared Black Michael, "wait 'til ye hear some o' th' others. His sermon on hell is a fret altogether! But the wan on courtin' bates Banagher. I tell ye what, there'll be a few fuckers hidin' at the back o' the gallery that day."

The schoolteacher, James Kierney, had remained in the church teaching catechism to the children. He had only recently been appointed and one of the strict conditions of his appointment was that he would take the children for instructions

45

every Sunday after mass. When he arrived at the gate the group was deferential to him and people passed pleasantries before the burning question was pitched.

"What do you think of Fr Glennon, sir?"

Mr Kierney had a habit of shaking his head. Some attributed the condition to nerves, others believed it was caused by a superfluity of brains. The twitching seemed to intensify as he pondered the question.

"A loose cannon," he replied simply and passed on his way.

There were puzzled looks at one another as the conclusion was gravely pondered.

"Whatever the hell that manes," someone observed.

"It means," ventured another with a reputation for learning, "that he's nearly as good as a bishop. A canon is very high up."

Thereafter he would be referred to informally as Canon Glennon, or the Canon. Jamesy Fitzhenry would be better known as Pontius Pilate and Paddy Simons as the Jew. Mary Julia Martin stylistically profited least from the experience but was occasionally ascribed the indecorous sobriquet of Lasher. The primal preoccupation of nicknaming, challenging but callous, flourishes according to the deprivation and ignorance of a society. Vacuous genesis enriches the art. In Geblik it was perfected.

As the group finally broke up on the sunny spring morning, crows cawed noisily in the nearby rookery. Other birds flew around or twitched inquisitively on walls and hedges. Cattle searched for pickings on bare pastures. The muted lows of a bulling cow intermittently resounded in the distance. Patches of brown in fields and rusted ploughs at headlands indicated that the tillage season had started. There was an ordinariness about the place, a sense of God-forsakenness and despondency that would register for different people at varying degrees. But Fr Glennon's petrifying oratorical performance brought a bewildering bustle that had been missing since Fr Straw's time. The new curate had made his indelible mark.

*

If the effect of a sermon could be determined by the ferment it created, Fr Glennon's exhortation deserved the ultimate rating. Outside the desperate fight for survival, where people were concerned mostly with humdrum affairs, there was no competition for attention; they thought and spoke about very little else. Groups dissected and interpreted the dynamic performance, often coming to contradictory conclusions.

Black Michael felt vindicated and proud that Fr Glennon had lived up to his high billing. But he had some reservations of a serious nature.

"What puzzles me," he said, "is how the hell can it be that Geblik is blamed for the Crucifixion and all the rest of it? I never went to no school but all of this was supposed to be done out foreign, and the four people he picked out never put a foot outside the country. And how the fuck could they be around that long ago when Adam was only a gosson? Shure it doesn't make sense, so it doesn't. No matter what Fr Glennon says I'd hold nothin' agin' any o' them.

"An' the idea of Mary Julia doin' the scourgin'! Begod, she wouldn't be fit to kick a dog in th'arse. I'm a long time lookin' at stations o' the cross and I never saw a woman with a whip in her hand in any o' the pictures."

"You got it all wrong, Black", someone explained. "He didn't accuse them of being personally responsible. What he meant was..."

"I don't give a damn what he meant," Black Michael retorted. "Didn't I see him pointing the finger straight at Mary Julia with my own two eyes!"

"Don't mind the Black," a more discerning associate advised in a low tone. "He's only a gobshite."

It reached Black Michael's ears as fully intended.

"Who's a gobshite?" he challenged in a loud voice. "Who's a gobshite?"

With a gesture of his hand Christy the Kithen Smiley calmed the threatening situation. He was a middle-aged man of many talents – builder, thatcher, healer and counsellor, for a start – who was also regarded as something of a philosopher. There were, of course, critics and begrudgers who questioned his authority. One doubting Thomas held that his notion of self import was such that he'd take on not alone to put an eye in a duck's arse and make it wink but to give it full vision as well. But Kithen's knowledge was based on impeccable sources – *Old Moore's Almanac, St. Colmcille's Prophecy, The Sayings of Poor Richard* and *The Writings of Kiddy Muldoon*, to name the most important. He had done a line for ten years or so with Mary Julia Martin but, strangely, his updated views on courting were diametrically different to hers. In fairness, she was not opposed to decent courting – brother and sister stuff as Micksheen the Blackguard would describe it – and proudly boasted that while she and Kithen kept company for ten years she never knew his weight, never even knew whether he was a man or a woman. He, on the other hand, succumbed to revisionist notions, possibly related to reflections on his manhood, and opined once (after uncharacteristically imbibing to excess at a wake) that passion was more important than propriety in the mating game.

Kithen spoke little but reflected much. As he moved to leave, in his rather pompous and ponderous way, he turned around and pushed the soft hat back on his head.

"Regarding this whole business of religion," he declared solemnly, "it's hard to know who the hell is the rale gobshites. I'll tell ye somethin', common sense and religion is like oil an' water – they don't mix well. There's people can only take religion in small doses. An' there's others can fatten on it."

Black Michael looked after him as he left. "That's a right bollox," he stated tersely, "if ever there was wan! He thinks he knows more than the pope in Rome. An' he knows as much about religion as an aul' cow knows about a holiday."

*

"Be the sufferin' Jaysus," Prick McGinnity swore, "religion is comin' to an awful pitch. I got hard penances in me time, the rosary a few times that the devil got into me. But to have to eat an onion every day for a penance is the last straw! What the fuck is the world comin' to?"

"You're right, Prick," Micksheen the Blackguard agreed. "People is being put off religion with one thing and another. The like of it was never heard before, eating onions for penance."

Christy the Kithen argued that devouring onions would be far more acceptable and civilised than the old custom of wearing sackcloth and ashes. His views, however, were not regarded as convincing.

The matter arose just one week after Fr Glennon's frightening sermon on Christ's passion in Holmogats. He was hearing confessions on Saturday night in the same church and there was a small group awaiting their turn kneeling outside the confession box under the women's gallery. Anyone with sharp ears could hear snatches of the whispered discourse between priest and penitent despite trying not to do so. That was the way it had always been in living memory but reluctant eavesdroppers invariably feigned obliviousness with impassive meditative poses. It was different on this occasion.

Cushy Bennett was the first into the box after Fr Glennon closed the door behind him. She was a widow in her fifties, somewhat hard of hearing, and would not be regarded as particularly pious or God-fearing. After a while, during which some garbled or incoherent discourse emanated from the confessional indicating that Cushy was troubled with temptations of a sensual nature, the clear voice of Fr Glennon could be heard.

"Take a raw onion every day, one onion a day."

Those waiting in the seats tensed but managed to retain an unaffected poise. However, when the penitent was about to emerge the priest's words were repeated in a higher and peremptory tone.

"Don't forget, eat a raw onion every day."

People looked sideways at one another and there were a few sharp nudges. Everyone assumed that this obligation was imposed as a penance. They were never to know that in mitigation of one of her dominant sins she had pleaded a chronic ailment and that Fr Glennon's directive related to this aspect, the body rather than the soul!

In coming to a conclusion about an appropriate tag for the new curate, all such matters were taken into account. His coldish, aloof personality was off-putting and he had no interest in secular or social activities that were very popular in the parish, like Gaelic football or the Irish language revival. It was evident to the least discerning that he could not be pigeonholed or fitted into any established category.

Nearly two weeks had elapsed when a group in the village pub was earnestly considering the matter. Divergent and contradictory views were forcefully expressed. Fr Glennon had his supporters as well as detractors.

Hughie the Thrush's summing up reflected the views of those who claimed the appointment was a blessing for the parish.

"He's a livin' saint," he claimed. "A very holy man."

Christy the Kithen's opinion was representative of others who believed that Fr Glennon's input would be totally negative.

"He's a terror," was his verdict. "There's no other way ye could describe him. A terror!"

Towards the end, when it appeared a consensus could not be reached, one of the sagacious debaters turned to the Twit Farrell, a young man regarded as half amadán.

"Well, Tomboy," he asked, simply to provide terminal merriment to the debate, "what do you think of Fr Glennon?"

"I think," was the considered reply, "that he's a holy terror!"

Whether the statement was a grovelling attempt to respect the two diametrically opposed points of view, an inspiration from the Holy Ghost, or simply a commonly used colloquial ejaculation, was a matter of indifference. It summed up the situation perfectly. And so that became the generic definition by which the new curate would be adjudged and remembered. A holy terror.

Not All Marriages Are Made In Heaven

Prologue

In its early and formative years the confessional Irish Free State identified, and concentrated on eliminating, the greatest exigent threat to morality and virtue – sex. Concern for sexual propriety was, therefore, top of the pietistic agenda, and anything that endangered chastity and probity was an anathema to be condemned and outlawed. By far the greatest menace in this regard was dancing. But women were becoming an increasingly intractable part of the alarming problem.

The Irish bishops in their Lenten Pastorals gave a clear picture of the Catholic Church's disquietude. These Pastorals were considered to have such important implications for society that from the 1920s to the 1960s they were carried annually by the *Irish Independent* daily newspaper. Taking the year 1924 as fairly typical, it is interesting to note a consensus regarding the prevalence of many abuses. Chief among these were women's immodest fashions in dress, indecent dances, unwholesome theatrical performances and cinema exhibitions, evil literature and drink, strikes and lockouts.

His Eminence, Cardinal Logue, stated: *"Men are now engaged in a laudable effort to restore peace and tranquility, to repair the wreck and ruin of the past, to build up the country materially and restore prosperity. These are laudable efforts, in which every man* of good will should earnestly co-operate.

"This, though most important, is a mere material reparation; but there is another reparation which is less thought of but infinitely more important, to bring back our people to a sense of peace, charity, honesty and obedience in all things to God's law. Upon this reparation depends eternity. There are some abuses to which I must reluctantly refer. The dress, or rather the want of dress of women, at the present day is a crying scandal. There seems to be a rivalry among them as to how little dress they can wear without incurring universal reprobation. We see enough of this in everyday life, but if we can judge from advertisements in the newspapers we do not see the worst. What shocks one most is to see persons presenting themselves for Holy Communion in these dresses. I have often felt an impulse to pass them over. In Rome lately, the Cardinal Vicar, no doubt with the approbation of the Pope, published a decree forbidding the clergy to give Holy Communion to those who present themselves in an unbecoming dress. I fear his example must be followed, if the scandal is to be stopped.

"Another abuse is dancing, especially all-night dances. Latterly, there seems to be a regular mania for dancing. As to the character of the dances, I know nothing, especially those imported dances, except some of the names which I see in the newspapers, and certainly the names are bizarre enough. Those who do know them tell me they are mostly objectionable on the score of morality. They seem to be the outcrop of the corruption of the age.

"Among other effects of the disorders through which we have passed is a serious falling away in the matter of temperance."

His Grace, the Most Rev. Dr Byrne, wrote: "It has often been said to be a characteristic of our people that they are gifted by God in an eminent degree with spiritual vision. If this be true, it is difficult to understand the feverish rush for pleasure which seems to absorb the minds and energies of so many at the present day. Innocent recreation and reasonable relaxation from work have never been discouraged by the Church; but she never fails to raise her voice in warning when she perceives that amusement is tending towards sin. Examples are not far to seek. Dancing, of course, is not intrinsically bad in itself, but it can become a prolific source of evil, if not conducted under the strictest supervision.

"Suggestive dances imported from countries whose outlook is largely pagan, dances which give offence to the eyes of onlookers, and – human nature being what it is – must often be a source of temptation to the performers, should be strictly banned by our Catholic people, and discouraged at gatherings of clean-minded boys and girls.

"Many of the abuses which are rife in our midst would soon be abolished if there were a sound, strong Catholic opinion operating amongst our people, which would not permit things offensive to Catholic feeling or dangerous to Catholic morals."

His Grace, the Most Rev. Dr Gilmartin, averred: "If company-keeping is an occasion of mortal sin there is no use in people going to Confession if they did not mean to give it up. If dances were the occasion of mortal sin there could be no repentance unless they stayed away from these dances. In recent years there had been too much of both. It would be altogether against the spirit of Lent to have dances during the sacred season. Those who at any season took part in introducing foreign corrupting dances were guilty of grave scandal. All who assisted in organising them or giving accommodation for them were guilty of co-operating in grave scandal.

"Of all the curses pronounced in Holy Scripture against evildoers the most awful were those hurled against scandal-givers."

Most Rev. Dr Fogarty felt people had "*become frivolous in*

their habits and views of life, excessively fond of amusement and pleasure, and dancing and drinking. Aversion to manual labour had become a disease. For the one man willing to work with his hands, hundreds were looking for petty clerkships and shop appointments."

Most Rev. Dr O'Doherty asserted that *"while occasional dances, of a modest kind, might well be excused, he would be a very lax moralist indeed who could hold that the dances, as now carried on, could be placed in that category. There was no proper supervision. The dances indulged in were not the clean, healthy, national Irish dances. They were, on the contrary, importations from the vilest dens of London, Paris and New York – direct and unmistakable incitements to evil thoughts, evil desires and grossest acts of impurity. For the average individual these fast dances were immediate occasions of sin."*

A few years later, Dr Gilmartin encapsulated the depressing causes of serious moral decline: *"In recent years the dangerous occasions of sin had been multiplied. The old Irish dances had been discarded for foreign importations which, according to all accounts, lent themselves not so much to rhythm as to low sensuality. The actual hours of sleep had been turned into hours of debasing pleasure. Company-keeping under the stars of night had succeeded in too many places to the good old Irish custom of visiting, chatting and story-telling from one house to another, with the rosary to bring all home in due time. Parental control had been relaxed, and fashions bordering on indecency had become a commonplace; while bad books, papers and pictures were finding their way into remote country places."*

In these years the critical emigration release option was around fifty-thousand per annum but, rather than condemn political ineptitude for this situation, the Catholic Church reserved its indignation for those who took the boat, accusing them of turning their backs on their country, and considered their destinations English dens of moral iniquity. The truth was that, because of cruel exploitation, any serious diminution of Ireland's social ills had always depended on the ultra evils of emigration, famine and pestilence.

How, one might wonder, did the dress, or want of dress of women, regarded as a crying scandal by Cardinal Logue, compare with the coercive indecent exposure in rags and tatters of countless numbers, over generations, because of imperial degeneracy and profligacy? What kind of analysing could conclude, compared to all the evils of social injustice, that imported dances were the outcrops of the corruption of the age? Clearly, clean-minded Christian boys and girls were vulnerable fodder to the shock influence of foreign suggestive and corrupting dances if left to their own resources. But rescue was at hand; the resources of the all-powerful Church of Rome, that had given Ireland to England in the twelfth century, were unerringly set against libertines and loafers and would be the arbiters in social and political conditioning.

*

In 1925, *The Meath Chronicle* reported:

"The modern young woman cannot be easy unless she has a man's job, and a man's trousers on (sic)." So declared Mr Tully at the meeting of Ceannanus Mór Urban Council in March, Mr P. Hopkins in the Chair. The remark was occasioned by a reference to government departments.

"It is very unfair," continued Mr Tully. "In ten years' time we'll have nothing in this unfortunate country but old maids and cats.

It is the greatest curse of Ireland to be having women in everything. Because they're cheeky and cheap they are succeeding in ousting the young men out of positions in every department of the public service, in the banks and in commercial undertakings. The government offices are crammed with women. Hence the young men are flying from the country as fast as they can go. If young men had these jobs they would, in time, be in a position to marry, but women in these positions seldom marry and, besides, men are afraid to marry that type of woman. Even in the National Trust a woman has been placed at the head of it. Are we going to be bossed by petticoats? Would you help a woman to the position of town clerk?"

Mr Reilly – No.

Mr Tully – Woman was made for one job by God Almighty, and she is a fool in her own interests if she does not stick to it.

In 1926, *The Meath Chronicle* had more disquieting news for its readers under the headings of 'Illegitimacy Scandal, Meath Board of Health's Action':

At the meeting of the Meath Board of Health on Wednesday, Mr P. Hopkins (chairman) presiding, a letter was read from the father of a girl in the Maternity Hospital Trim, refusing to take her out and suggesting that proceedings be taken for maintenance against the father of the girl's baby who, he said, was in employment and could drink his earnings. Mr Duffy said he had a resolution prepared that statements be taken from all these girls and the suggested fathers be proceeded against. He understood there were thirty or thirty-five of these unfortunate girls in the Trim institution, and it was time to bring those responsible for their condition to book. The ratepayers paid for the maintenance of the girls brought to misfortune and paid for the maintenance of their children while those responsible get off scot free.

The Irish Free State was not alone in its fanatical mission of stabilising appropriate sexual norms, as is evident from the following brief report published in *The Meath Chronicle* in 1927, 'Charleston Dancing Ban – Drastic Action in Turkey and Italy':

A war on the dancing craze has been begun by the authorities in Italy and Turkey. All dancing halls are being closed down in both countries 'for reasons of public morality'. Signor Mussolini has begun a new crusade against the dance craze. On New Year's Eve an order was issued forbidding dancing at such places in Rome, and the Premier has extended the order to the whole of Italy. Prefects all over the country have been instructed to close altogether all dancing cabarets, tabarins, and night clubs 'for reasons of public morality'.

With a view to safeguarding the morals of the youth of both sexes, the police authorities at Constantinople have decided to close all dancing halls, licenses for which have only been granted since Mustapha Kemel established the government at Angora. Most of these places, while frequented by young women of good family, as well as by students, were also the resort of loose women. By this decision it is hoped to check a wave of depravity which has been threatening the youth of Constantinople recently. In Angora, youths and girls under 18 are not allowed in the ordinary cinema, special houses having been set aside for them.

*

The Catholic Church's primary concern about a perceived lowering standard of sexual morality in Ireland, a concern criticised by all serious commentators, was withal logical and understandable, however deplorable and regressive. This was an area, basic to existence, where the Church had engineered a monopoly, and any diminution of its power in this domain would be rightly considered a calamitous setback. Such a development would escalate and extend to other teachings with consequent impairment of the Church's influence, so a frantic and a desperate stand was inevitable to prevent a snowballing, knock-on effect.

Ireland's continued spiritual domination by Rome had been reinforced by Britain's colonial tyranny. The Cromwellian settlement was not a plantation in the ordinary sense of the term. It transferred the sources of wealth and power from Catholics to Protestants. But the great masses of the poor were left largely undisturbed – the landless peasants and the hopeless paupers. This mass of human rejects was betrayed by the indifference of boorish Christianity as well as a callous State: how, for example – and leaving aside such notorious issues as the Penal Laws – could the clearances, when families were thrown wholesale on the side of the road and their hovels levelled behind them, be equated with caring Christian values? How – and even overlooking Britain's responsibility for the horrendous effects of the Great Famine – could a government be regarded as consistent, serious and honourable, that on the one hand introduced progressive laws to improve health and living conditions, and on the other fostered a system that treated the majority of human beings as pernicious riff-raff to be barbarously eradicated, whose very existence thwarted progress? The hordes of Catholics in Ireland, who seldom or never saw the inside of the small thatched, mud-walled churches that dotted the countryside, were callously coerced and corralled by a morbid fear for the hereafter, as a palliative antidote for desperation with the present. Cruel, rapacious laws prevented destitute mortals from ever reaching the level of decency to which brute animals were entitled. What would have happened if Protestantism and Catholicism were not at hand to suffuse and exploit the immoral void is only a matter of academic diversion. The Catholic Church's mission impacted on social justice as a brake rather than the engine.

Up to 1785 there was a slow but very steady population increase in Ireland. From around that time it began to soar at an extraordinary rate. Irish peasants were conditioned by their spiritual leaders, and also by their wretched plight, to marry early. T. Campbell in *A Philosophical Survey of the South of Ireland,* 1777, stated: *"The manner in which the poor of the country live, I cannot help calling beastly. For upon the same floor, and frequently without any partition, are lodged the husband and wife, the multitudinous brood of children, all huddled together upon the straw or rushes, with the cow, the calf, the pig and the horse, if they are rich enough to have one."*

Marriages resulted from astute barter and bargaining, like the sale of an animal, and were arranged by parents without any regard for personal attraction or affection, the couple sometimes meeting for the first time at the nuptial altar. The process was an immutable shackle whereby often an immature boy and girl became husband and wife, stud and brood mare, licensed to copulate and obligated to propagate unremittingly together. They did not have the privacy of their own room or space to share intimacies, and while social commentators may dispute the main reason, or reasons, for the aforementioned population explosion, one fact is beyond dispute: coital stimulation involved time and kinetic activity on a massive scale. The conjugal act was effectively a communal experience, as animals in wild life. Outside the hovels there was no space, shelter or seclusion to answer the calls of nature, and the animal instinct again prevailed in the grossly over-crowded conditions. Regard for hygiene and sanitation was non-existent; people defecated and urinated publicly wherever a footing could be found in the expanding, putrescent cesspool. Fighting for survival left no time to waste on considering human dignity.

Intensive breeding co-existed with enforced asceticism for the many who were conventionally neutered. The coarsening of human nature could hardly be more comprehensive. Whether the Church was inherently devoid of a progressive social conscience or whether such a function had been hijacked is merely speculative; as always, social betterment was dependent on secular influences, which in Ireland's case had been ruthlessly subverted.

As the years passed conditions improved, helped paradoxically by the ravages of adversity. Also progressive endeavours had a rationale as an inducement to loyalty and peace, rather than a purely altruistic purpose. At the formation of the Irish Free State, however, there still remained a considerable heritage of perverse subhuman baggage.

End of Prologue

Although Geblik might always be at the very bottom of diocesan lists as regards records of significance, such as size, population, monetary contributions, achievements and the like, nevertheless it was a parish that was as deeply rooted in history and tradition as any other. In the struggle for freedom there were endless numbers prepared to fight and sacrifice their lives for their country, a disposition that puzzled Prick McGinnity.

"How the hell," he mused, "could men without work, that don't own a square inch of land, want to fight and die for Ireland? What do they owe to the country, for Christ's sake! Fr Straw's volunteers and them that fought the Black and Tans in Geblik had nothin'. Did the farmers or them that owned anything go out to fight? Why would they when the stupid hoors with not a plot to plant a spud on did it for them?"

Christy the Kithen had a different, a more profound and sympathetic, viewpoint. "They fought, and were prepared to die," he claimed, "not for what some people owned, but to get for others what they themselves were denied. The sacrifices they made were mostly for those who would come after them. They wanted change and there was only one way to get it. And by God they got the wheels movin', God bless them."

Although the basic instinct for survival was the dominant consideration there was also a muted or restricted spirit of neighbourliness and concern for others. With many exceptions of a more generous nature, though, the prevailing mood was class ossification, to keep people in their places. Everything combined to make social climbing impossible, but in instances where some individuals were so inclined devious resourceful pressures were effectively applied. There was an inherent desire to keep the head of a drowning rat above the water but not help it to reach a safe or privileged position on the bank.

Life dragged on. While never reaching the summit or enjoying glory, Gaelic football teams made their mark at senior grade despite all the odds, and there were athletes who distinguished themselves at county and provincial level. On the bleaker side, there was endemic poverty, hunger, malnutrition and the maladies which these conditions cause. Consumption was prevalent and a constant cause of terror. There were always individuals whose reputations were clouded for various reasons. Then, of course, there were charlatans and tricksters, some of whom were not entirely without virtue and often added an entertaining dimension to a bleak social milieu.

Whether reasonable or otherwise, Geblik had a strong sense of its own importance, people were proud of the place that gave them birth. Prick McGinnity might ask what on earth were they proud of, but Christy the Kithen had the answer to that – *the savage loves his native shore!* This feeling of consequence emanated to different degrees from diverse considerations, but without doubt it was epitomised and strengthened in a universal, hallowed regard for the priests of the parish. In consequence, apart from the spiritual significance, there was a social substrate committed to offering unconditional respect to the clergy, whatever their faults or foibles might be. Whether they were hardline purists or autonomous, wayward overlords made no difference; respect for every and any priest was unequivocal and wholehearted.

Idiosyncrasies and weaknesses might be mocked or exaggerated, but the priest was there to be respected and obeyed. Any serious breach in this regard was taboo, and would not be tolerated by a compliant laity.

*

The parochial house, where the parish priest and curate normally resided, was effectively the epicentre of the parish. At this time, however, and for a few years beforehand, the parish priest of Geblik had been confined to a medical institution and an administrator, Fr Joseph Drake, was in charge. Fr Peter Glennon, often referred to in the third person as the Canon, was the curate.

The housekeeper was Lena Cowley, a reserved lady in her late thirties, and the priest's boy was Peter Halligan aged around twenty-five years. Both were dedicated and trustworthy servants, basic requirements for engagement in such an establishment. Activities or transactions of a confidential nature that took place within the parochial arena – and there were many – were never discussed outside, or if they were the descriptions were appropriately edited. Ms Cowley resided in the parochial house. Peter Halligan lived at home close by and looked after the yard and gardens. He milked the two cows and fed the few calves on the attached field, among his various vocational assignments. Claims by a few carpers, irked by his authority and officiousness, that he would take on to hear confessions in cases of necessity, were without foundation.

The esteemed squad of parish priest, curate, housekeeper and priest's boy constituted what was regarded as the complete and ultimate manipulative inner circle of the Church in the parish. It would appear unrealistic to consider that anyone else might be added to that august body, and yet it happened, casually and without connivance of any kind. Marcus Clerkin was destined by providence to become an important fifth player – albeit in a part-time capacity only.

*

Marcus Clerkin was nearly twenty years of age in 1925 when his father purchased a posh, bull-nosed Morris Cowley motor car, with a let-down hood, and capable of travelling at speeds of up to fifty miles per hour. High speeds were rarely possible, however, due to the poor state of the green roads. Blue coloured, with canvas top and two windscreens, the car had no gear lever, just two pedals and a double clutch. It was purchased from Denny Nee, an enterprising garage proprietor in the neighbouring town of Skell, less than four miles distant. As part of his business Mr Nee purchased second-hand cars in England and imported them into Northern Ireland. On delivery of a car he would take two of his mechanics daily to dismantle it, bringing with them sufficient sustenance – a couple of loaves of bread, butter and a gallon of porter. They transported the dismembered parts across the border into the Irish Free State and reassembled them there to avoid tax duty. Any additional or replacement parts required for the Morris Cowley could be purchased from Joyce and Brady, Lemon Street, off Grafton Street, in Dublin.

Marcus Clerkin lived within a couple of hundred yards of Geblik parish church, and less than a quarter of a mile from the parochial house. Clerkins were respected, small but thrifty and comfortable farmers. Marcus worked on the home farm, and, being the eldest of a family of eight, four sons and four daughters, he had the responsibility of driving and looking after the car. His father never drove it as he was not mechanically inclined, but more significantly he was deterred by the increasing dangers and responsibilities inherent in motoring. Seldom a week went by without a car passing on the road. There were three other cars in the parish at this time and there was an expectation that the number would increase.

While attending the national school, Marcus had served on the altar. Only boys or male adults could serve mass. In cases where they were not available girls or women might act as witnesses, but always outside the altar rails; they could not encroach on the sanctuary. Sunday masses were celebrated in the church with large attendances. Particular weekday masses were also conducted in the church. But most daily masses were offered in the parochial house for obvious pragmatic reasons, including that, with a few exceptions, there seldom would be more than two or three worshippers in attendance. At the age of fourteen, when he finished schooling, and as was the usual practice, Marcus ceased to serve regularly on the altar. But because of the difficulty of getting acting servers to attend at the parochial house, and having regard to his obliging disposition, flexibility in respect of time, and proximity to the place, he found himself constrained to continue acting as mass server there. This took up a considerable amount of time in the mornings because it was not unusual for him to have to get the officiating priest out of bed as well. Where Fr Drake was concerned, this was difficult enough, but with the curate, Fr Glennon, it bordered on the impossible. Marcus, therefore, became more intimately acquainted with the priests than was anyone else in the parish. Also, since neither priest owned a car, a routine developed whereby they got him to drive them nearly everywhere. If either priest got stranded away from home the postmistress from Carnalstown, Julia Clynch, would arrive posthaste with a telegram requisitioning collection at a specified time. Because of this, many late evenings and nights were devoted to the concerns of their distinguished reverences.

Marcus Clerkin was a stockily built young man, intelligent and pleasant, with a quiet disposition, a lad of few words in any company. The clerical calls on his time were very demanding but whether or not he resented the never-ending solicitations was an issue nobody ever knew.

As far as Marcus was concerned, the main problem with the two priests was their fondness for drink. But at twenty years of age he could not be expected to understand the exigencies of human nature. A more mature and rational person would recognise that their alcoholism, as is generally the case, was situationally engendered. How any two well-educated men in an impoverished, God-forsaken cultural backwater, without any outlet for interests or stimulation, perpetually committed to moral policing and mostly futile persuasion, could remain sane or normal – never mind sober – is a notion that only those with a strong spiritual or religious bias could uphold or understand. Include the further important consideration of means: while invariably having to present themselves respectably, the capricious income of the priest was paltry in the extreme – that of the curate approximating to the wage of a casually employed farm labourer.

Although both priests imbibed regularly to excess, they rarely gave scandal. This was mainly because the drinking usually took place at night or late evening. Whenever over-indulgence occurred during a daytime visit to one of the upper-class families, the priest would normally be conveyed home by pony and trap. Thus the ordinary parishioner was unaware that the problem was so severe, although some difficulties were reported to have arisen on a few occasions when a priest was requisitioned for a sudden sick call. It was also common knowledge that on his cycling excursions through the village Fr Glennon would visit one or other of the two public houses and enjoy a quiet drink alone in the parlour.

In most other dioceses the parish priest and curate lived in separate dwellings, rather than both living in the one house. There are compelling arguments for and against both systems. One strong contra-claim concerns serious difficulties with relationships. Where two affable priests lived together, one elderly and the other young, there seldom was a communications problem, or if there was it could be sorted out satisfactorily. Where two mature priests were around the same age, one secure in the normally highest rank for secular clergy – a parish priest – and the other, for reasons best known to the bishop, destined to remain a curate for the rest of his life, discord and arguments were almost inevitable. Add in a grumpy disposition, the effects of drink and debilitating ailments, and the result could be a potentially explosive concoction. And that was the unfortunate, prevailing position in Geblik.

There were constant rows between Fr Drake and Fr Glennon, and these were particularly acrimonious after prolonged or unrestrained periods of drink. On one occasion, Fr Glennon struck Fr Drake with a smashing blow to the head. Fr Drake fell against the fire grate, and lay stretched on the floor, seemingly unconscious. When Fr Glennon came over to him, to check his condition, Fr Drake suddenly swung around with the poker and knocked out Fr Glennon. He had a red, swollen face as a result, and when people inquired what caused the disfiguration he blamed it on sunburn – at a rather overcast period in winter!

On another occasion, Marcus drove Fr Drake to a high mass

in Skell. He had to wait until mass ended and then drive him a couple of miles to the parochial house in Narcaross, where he left him and returned home. Later that evening he got a telegram to collect the priest. When he called to the parochial house Fr Drake was lying on the floor.

"Get up you so-and-so," Fr Kelly, the parish priest in Narcaross remonstrated with him. "I brought you in from where you fell in the hedge and when you got me out on a sick call you drank a full bottle of whiskey!"

Marcus took Fr Drake home to the parochial house in Geblik and, with great difficulty, got him into the parlour where he left him lying in a stupor on the sofa.

At another time, Fr Drake was too drunk to go on a sick call so Marcus travelled out the road to get Fr Glennon, who was doing his usual patrol. He told the priest he had to make the sick call.

"Why did Drake not go?" he asked. "Was he too drunk?"

"I don't know whether he's drunk or not," Marcus replied.

There was another row about the matter next day, and Fr Glennon pressurised Marcus to sign a statement claiming that Fr Drake was drunk and unable to fulfil his duty at the time, but he resolutely refused to do so.

*

It would be difficult to tabulate all the credibility problems and contentious issues that emerged in the parish of Geblik. They arose mostly spontaneously from time to time, but were mainly transient in nature, although there were concerns that agonised and lingered as well as those of purely diversionary character.

A few years earlier, reports of miracles at Knock had stirred up religious fervour in the parish. These extraordinary happenings were mulled over at a crowded public house in Carnalstown and there was a bitter argument regarding the actual number of persons raised from the dead. The upshot of the exchanges was that it was decided to make a collection and dispatch Lame Markey to Knock to avail of the healing largesse. Joe Markey was a bachelor in his fifties who had been incapacitated with a straight left leg for nearly thirty years.

Within a month a collection had been made and a donkey and cart purchased. Amid great excitement and expectations, Lame Markey waved back to the large crowd gathered for his departure and bravely set out on the journey of nearly one-hundred miles. Isaac Jenkens, a Protestant who owned the weighbridge on the Fair Green, declared publicly that he would become a Catholic if Joe Markey returned cured of the lame leg. There were great hopes of a miraculous conversion as well as a cure.

Unfortunately, Markey let the side down badly. He only got as far as Mellclonon, about twelve miles distant, where he sold the donkey and cart and spent all the proceeds on drink. To compound the offence, he claimed to be the victim of a robbery while he was asleep. Later he received a summons to attend court in Garmullin for driving an unlighted vehicle after dark. Isaac Jenkens, in the circumstances, could hardly be blamed for remaining faithful to his Protestant beliefs.

Peter Halligan, the priest's boy, had an experience that he found disconcerting. He was coming back from doing a job in the church on a sunny summer afternoon when he noticed Fr Drake and the housekeeper, Lena Cowley, walking down the field at the back of the parochial house. He was tempted to call after them to see what they were about, in case there was an animal in difficulty or a fence needing immediate attention. Since they were walking at a rather leisurely pace he desisted and watched them as they disappeared behind the hill, from which they should reappear shortly. But to his consternation it was nearly a half-hour before they came into sight. What were they doing? He was never to know. It was a beautiful evening to stand chatting at a gateway enjoying the sunshine. Furthermore, there seemed little sense in favouring the open fields to the privacy of the parochial house if an impropriety were involved. And yet he could not control the wicked thoughts that passed through his troubled mind and would return sporadically to afflict him afterwards.

Fr Glennon had a dislike for families that kept bulls, buck goats or cocks for breeding hire. He would not attend mass stations at these places. When Fr Drake carried out the function at one such a location, Fr Glennon accosted him.

"You did the station."

"I had to when you wouldn't."

"I could smell the bull off you before you got to the gate!"

There was some evidence of inter-parish co-operation at clerical level. Fr Hacklin, the parish priest in Nalmoyty, caught Cock Casey from Geblik courting a girl within his jurisdiction. A short time afterwards the Cock was with a group of youths outside the school, which was beside the parochial house, when he got a message that Fr Glennon wanted to see him.

"He must want his hair cut," he declared, at the same time suspecting the purpose of the summons. When he stepped inside the door Fr Glennon grabbed him by the throat, but he managed to get outside where he picked up a handful of stones and threw them back in the direction of the enraged curate.

Confession with Fr Glennon was particularly daunting. He whispered in a rather high tone and penitents had to do likewise, with the result that people in the church could hear snatches of proceedings. On several occasions he left the confession box and followed penitents to their seats where he admonished them severely. Another time, when Cock Casey was at confession, those outside the confession box could hear his warning.

"You're going to end up in a lunatic asylum if you're not careful!"

Fr Drake, on the other hand, was in some respects more worldly-wise than spiritually inclined. One Saturday afternoon, when he was hearing confessions in the church, rain suddenly began to pour and the housekeeper sent the priest's boy with an umbrella to him. While listening to the sins of a penitent, Fr Drake noted Peter Halligan coming up the aisle and realised the purpose of his visit.

"Don't mind me," he shouted out. "Look after the sick calf – did you put him in out of the rain?"

There was a mission in the parish lately, given by the Vincentians from Phibsborough in Dublin. Fr McElligot and Fr Kelly were the two priests involved. Marcus Clerkin had the responsibility of driving Fr McElligot to Holmogats in the mornings to celebrate mass in the chapel of ease and preach the sermon. He found him temperamental and unpredictable. One morning, the priest ordered him on the journey home to give a lift to children on their way to school. The following morning when he was pulling up to do the same, Fr McElligot scolded him and told him to drive on without the children!

As Christy the Kithen said, common sense and religion are like oil and water – they don't mix well. There's a lot of believing that has to be swallowed with a grain of salt, he claimed.

*

Despite the unseemly capers that Marcus Clerkin witnessed in the parochial house, and that were hidden from the outside world, there were protracted periods of calm, even ardour, as well. On these occasions the housekeeper could emerge from behind the barricaded kitchen door and attend to her duties with all the appearance of normality.

It was at such a time, after serving morning mass, that Fr Glennon indicated to Marcus that he would require his chauffeuring service that evening.

"Do you know that blackguard, Jamesy Fitzhenry from Roigeen?" he inquired.

"I do, Father," Marcus replied. "He's working at the present time, I believe, cleaning ditches for Tom Kangley in the Cushogs. A tough, awkward, ignorant man," he added in warning.

"Well I want to see him this evening. Call for me at the church around three o'clock. I'll tame the scoundrel and put a hop in his gallop!"

"All right, Father, I'll be there," Marcus assured him, knowing full well the delicate purpose of the mission. It was common knowledge that Nancy Mulligan was in trouble and Jamesy Fitzhenry was the man alleged to be responsible.

*

Jamesy Fitzhenry was an attractive and amiable young labouring man of twenty-five years. But he could pass as the son of a farmer or shopkeeper because, even against a background of appalling poverty and social deprivation, his outlook and attitude were removed from the generic grovelling mores of a passing peasant culture. There were two main reasons for this. Firstly, the entrenched slave disposition of the underprivileged in Ireland was crumbling under the pressures of nationalist success and fervour. Secondly, he was a remarkably intelligent, complex, intractable and unpredictable character.

He was five foot, nine inches tall, of medium build, handsome, with a fresh complexion, brown eyes and thick crop of brown hair, variously combed back or cropped close. Good natured and honest, but extremely volatile, he was unsurpassable as a labourer and so was seldom out of work, even in the hopelessly bad times. The youngest of a family of ten, he lived with his widowed mother in a county council cottage which had been acquired long before he was born when a thatched hovel in which the family resided caved in. Apart from a sister and brother, both married, the seven others – one brother and six sisters – had died before the age of twenty from the national scourge, consumption. His living brother, Harry, a giant of a man, was regarded as the second strongest man in the parish; he could lift a barrel of wheat weighing twenty stone up off the ground to a platform and then on to his back. Matt Kernan, the strongest man, while less impressive in stature, could nevertheless lift the same bag straight on to his back without any platform. The paradox of such brute strength and consumptive weakness within the Fitzhenry family was not lost on reflective members of the impoverished community.

Jamesy's mother, Brigid, was married at the age of fourteen to a man nearly four times older. She was widowed at the age of twenty-six, and there was seldom, if ever, a time when there was sufficient food to go on the table. In the springtime she planted spuds and could dig furrows all day to match her son, Harry. During summer she dug and saved the turf. At harvest time she cut the corn with a reaping hook. Long days and nights were also spent working the spinning wheel and knitting. Hardship and suffering had made her cynical and tough. But a hard exterior and sharp words were only a fragile shell, cover for a soul that was ravaged and broken but unyielding to the end.

Of all the children, and the sadness they brought, Jamesy was the one who unceasingly broke his mother's heart. While the others would respond to a slap or admonition for being disobedient or naughty, such reproofs had no effect on Jamesy. He was incorrigible. His mother soon learned it was best to leave him to his own devices, even though frustrated neighbours condemned her for losing control of the brazen brat.

At school, although he mitched a lot, the teachers reported that he was exceptionally bright. But he was far from a model pupil. Of all the children in the class he didn't turn up for the catechetical examination before confirmation, so with great annoyance to the parish priest and principal he had to be examined on the day by the bishop, who gave him a number one. Then, at the age of thirteen, his primary school career came to an abrupt and ignominious end. The principal of the school was a very strict gentleman who had a reputation for inflicting severe corporal punishment as an inducement to discipline and learning. Jamesy, for some deficiency, found himself targeted for a heavy caning and decided against enduring it. He made a bolt for the door but the teacher was adroit enough to cut off that way of escape. Without losing momentum Jamesy jumped on a seat by the wall and crashed through one of the high windows, knocking a sash off its hinges. Unfortunately, there was a barrel full of water beside the window on the path outside and Jamesy fell head first into it. Luckily, the shocked teacher was able to extricate him promptly and ordered him home directly to change his saturated clothing. His home was about half a mile distant. When his mother saw him she was appalled and questioned him about the calamity. He gave her an edited version of the story to the effect that the teacher had tried to drown him in a barrel of water. Brigid, like everyone in the parish, was well aware of the teacher's penchant for inflicting physical abuse but she felt that, whatever the circumstances, attempted murder should not be tolerated. She sent an urgent message to her son, Harry, who the following day burst into the school and in front of terrified pupils grabbed the petrified teacher by the throat. Children raced out into the yard roaring, "He's killing the teacher, he's killing him!" Workers near the school reacted to the alarm and the rescued teacher was able to give a factual account of the fortuitous drowning which somewhat pacified the enraged aggressor. Few people felt sorry for Jamesy. "Pity the bugger didn't drown," was a melodramatic viewpoint endorsed by many. There was no criticism of the teacher.

When Jamesy left school he worked with various farmers for a pittance but he built up a reputation as a hard and honest worker who was sometimes difficult to control. At seventeen years of age he progressed to the rank of ploughman and got a job, which would be of long duration, with Michael Dunny, who was a substantial and progressive farmer. But his life always seemed to be jinxed and, through unusual circumstances, he was sacked within a few hours of starting. He began work at eight o'clock on a Monday morning and took the two horses to the outlying field where he yoked them up and started to plough. Later in the morning the peace and quietness of the countryside was broken with bugling, cries and yelping, and he got excited realising from the loudening sounds that a hunt was fast approaching. Within a short space of time a fox dashed across the lower part of the field pursued by hounds and horses ridden by multicoloured riders of assorted shapes and sizes. The excitement was too much for him to resist. In a jiffy he had the two horses unyoked and tied the Clydesdale to the plough. He unharnessed the Irish draught, jumped up on its back and, with the peak of his cap pulled down behind his head, and whooping like a trooper, galloped with abandon until he caught up with the main body of the hunt. He careered to the front, jumping fences and ditches where others sought gaps or gateways. After about an hour the fox went to ground and Jamesy, on a tired horse, covered in frothing sweat, set out by road on the journey home. When he reached the ploughfield Michael Dunny was there waiting for him. Not a word was spoken, but the look on Michael Dunny's face as he pointed to the gate conveyed the clear message. Jamesy threw a ragged coat over his shoulder, started whistling a lively tune and kicked a few clods with abandon as he departed.

As well as being strong and resilient, Jamesy had an intellect that set him apart. He was in his early twenties when a circus came to Carnalstown that featured novel contests. One of these was a greasy pig competition. A strong young pig, smeared all over with butter or grease, would be released in the ring and members of the audience were invited to catch and hold on to the animal. Anyone who succeeded in doing so would get the pig as a prize. The circus stayed for three nights and, despite valiant efforts by strong contenders, amid scenes of unprecedented hilarity, nobody could perform the feat. Most competitors could catch the animal but not one could hold on to it. The second last competitor on the third night was Matt Kernan, who made desperate attempts but all to no avail – it was impossible to get a grip on the slippery animal. Last man to try was Jamesy Fitzhenry. To the consternation of the circus personnel as well as the spectators, he held the pig for longer than the stipulated two minutes while both tumbled together madly through the ring.

When asked afterwards how he managed to perform the feat he had no hesitation in sharing the secret.

"I had to get a grip in two places," he explained, "so I got a left-hand finger into its mouth and a right-hand finger up its arse, and the divil wouldn't loosen it!"

Even the host of begrudgers could not suppress a sneaking regard for the sole winner, however ridiculous or banal the exercise. But what pleased them greatly was that Jamesy's hold on the pig was tenuous enough in the end; the animal was stolen after the show while he was having a few celebratory drinks in an overcrowded pub.

It was a time of unprecedented social flux, surreally upbeat. Although Patrick Pearse's maternal forebears were natives of the parish of Geblik, there had been little serious local involvement with the 1916 Rising. But Sinn Féin influence was strong, the Gaelic League was well supported, jail sentences for illegal drilling and possession of arms were common, police barracks and mansions owned by adherents of Britain were despoiled or burned down and ranch lands rendered unmanageable. Despite British military might and the perfidious peelers, national Ireland was unrestrainable.

Jamesy Fitzhenry was caught up in the exhilarating and irresistible secessionist mood of the time. He left school at thirteen and became deeply involved in activities of a rebellious nationalist nature. Enthusiasm and availability ensured that his help was enlisted frequently, and often when a more mature volunteer might be considered prudent.

Within his short lifetime a dormant hope had been activated by circumstances that related variously to local, national and international affairs. Not all the features of those events were entirely positive but the broad swing was unquestionably upbeat.

Included in the fusion would be the World War, the 1916 Rising, the Troubles and the Anglo-Irish Treaty which created the Irish Free State. Subheadings would include Britain's major blunder in the executions of Irish patriots, the callous reprisals, censorship, prohibition proclamations and intimidations. Organisations like the Gaelic League and representatives for land reform also played a big part. But undoubtedly the input that ensured success was contributed by Sinn Féin.

Like many other young men at the time, Jamesy's disposition was strongly anti-British and events strengthened his resolve. His mother had been shocked when, while he was digging in their roadside garden, he defiantly brandished a spade at a passing convoy of Black and Tans. His first attendance in a minor role at a Sinn Féin court impressed him deeply. The judge was a road-worker from an adjoining parish and those before the court were obliged to address him as 'your worship' in accordance with protocol. A majority of those appearing before him had to be reproved as they were prone to use his first name, Mickey. One lady had a case against her neighbour whose goats, it was claimed, had destroyed a laurel hedge by eating and paring the bark of the mature shrubs near the ground.

"Your worship," pleaded the aggrieved lady, "you'll see the destruction plainly for yourself the next time you're around scraping the dirt off the side of the road."

The judge, knowing both parties well, gladly availed of the suggestion to defer making a decision until he saw the alleged havoc at some future uncommitted date. Jamesy marvelled at the adroitness of the man as well as the pomp and solemnity of the occasion.

While Jamesy was attending an adult Irish class one night in the village an RIC officer burst into the room and menacingly faced the teacher.

"I proclaim this meeting over," he declared, with an authority that, in other times, would be obeyed immediately, without question.

There was a pause as those attending, of which Jamesy would be the youngest, closed their small Fr O'Growney Irish grammar books and awaited directions from the teacher. Before this could happen Tom Casey, a sturdy middle-aged man who, during drinking sessions, bragged of a relationship to the world champion wrestler, Steve Casey, faced the police officer and, with a smashing right hand punch to the jaw, left him flattened on the floor. Slowly and awkwardly, the man got to his feet, replaced his hat and dusted himself before disappearing gingerly through the door. The episode was illustrative of undermined and irreversibly smitten peeler power and influence in Ireland.

At election times timorous democracy was stiffened by the presence of dour characters reputed to have guns, in the vicinity of certain polling booths. While impoverishment remained a persisting reality, there was a heady feeling that Ireland's freedom and better times were at last in sight, and Jamesy Fitzhenry, while a fairly inconsequential figure in the enfolding drama, was a paradigm example of the mood prevalent in a new generation.

He was outgoing and gregarious, could take a drink, sing a song (from a repertoire mostly concerned with Ireland's fight for freedom), and take part in sporting activities without ever considering participation or achievements too seriously. One attribute for which he was particularly noted was a sharp and often acerbic wit – he never allowed feeling or friendship to come in the way of a good line or provocative comment. Like most other young men he had a fondness for dancing, cycling and walking to venues near and far. Inevitably, his name was associated with stories of romances, some of which led to enforced marriages involving other men. But no serious paternal issue confronted him until Nancy Mulligan became pregnant. They had met at house dances and intermittently between. She was four years his senior, and he had other partners that were higher on his preferential list. So when the hullabaloo arose he suspended whatever affection or attraction had motivated him, sought to terminate the liaison and set himself mulishly to weather the storm.

Any woman in such a predicament faced impossible and frightening obstacles. But where the man concerned was acclaimed for callousness and obduracy only a miraculous intervention could resolve the dilemma. Nancy Mulligan had a desperate struggle before her to keep a grip on honour and decency.

*

Nancy Mulligan was twenty-eight years of age and had worked as housekeeper with O'Raleighs in the big house since she left the national school. Christopher Thomas O'Raleigh, invariably given the appellation Mister by the wider community but variously referred to as CT or the Boss at a more intimate level, farmed over two-thousand acres of land reputed to be the best in Ireland. Three other women also worked full-time in the mansion, as well as a servant boy and a valet-cum-chauffeur. Four or five men were employed in the yard and over twenty on the farm. While some of the other important families in the parish had an exclusive right to pews in the church, the O'Raleighs claimed a whole gallery that had not to be shared with the common crowd. Clearly, the O'Raleigh dynasty was a prestigious establishment and everyone employed there was obliged to behave with the decorum appropriate to such an esteemed institution. An abiding servile loyalty was also a *sine qua non*.

Employment on the estate was generally a hereditary affair, passing to sons and daughters of tried and trusted workers. To be on the payroll was a measure of prestige. It was also materially attractive, having a permanent income through bad times. Pay was always relatively good, free fuel in the form of timber and coal was provided for every worker and animals were killed at Christmas time and Easter to bestow generous presents of meat and bacon.

Nancy Mulligan's father had worked all his life as a valued and trusted herder on the farm so when the time came for her to seek service it was almost a foregone conclusion that she would be engaged at the big house. But although special concessions applied in such cases to the families of employees, there was still the important consideration of upholding standards, and it was made clear to Nancy that she would have to work for a probationary period before a decision could be made on approval for a permanent position. There was nothing unusual in this arrangement and the fourteen-year-old child was determined to work her hardest to impress. It transpired, however, that she almost failed at the first hurdle.

When she reported for work on a Monday morning Mrs O'Raleigh, generally reverentially referred to as the Mistress, sat her down in the parlour and described in considerable detail the obligations attached to the position. Honesty, commitment, punctuality and reputation were issues that were basic. Also, any tasks undertaken would have to be carried out to perfection; shoddy or inferior work would not be acceptable under any circumstances – Nancy would be in the employment of a gentleman and her behaviour and attitude should reflect that situation. The demands did not seem unreasonable to the child, who, in any event, had been forewarned regarding the main issues. She was then given her first task: to clean a large blackened pot in the scullery and to take it to the Mistress for examination when completed. There was no set period as regards time but proficiency was of the essence.

For nearly two hours she sanded, scrubbed and washed the vessel until it gleamed like new. Then, with assurance, she knocked on the parlour door and presented herself for approbation before the Mistress. She was crestfallen to be told that her effort was not acceptable and to try again. It was the same story the next time, and for several more occasions. At around four o'clock in the afternoon, with her nails worn to the flesh and the pot burnished like glass, she got the same response. Weary and dejected, with tears rolling down her cheeks, she was on her way back to the scullery when she met the boss. He inquired what was the matter and she explained to him that she could not scour the burner any cleaner or brighter.

"Maybe that's not the problem," he suggested to her. "It could be yourself. Try washing and drying your hands the next time."

She did so without delay, and this time the Mistress was very complimentary.

"Excellent, Nancy," was her only comment.

But she was soon to learn that although the Mistress was particular and aloof, she was fond of gossip and was as abreast of all local activities as any of the servants. Nancy progressed in her position and her genial nature endeared her to all with whom she came in contact. Young children who called to the big house to collect the free milk or for other messages never left while she was on duty without a round of a loaf or cake buttered and jammed. None of the other servants had this considerate touch, and so such visits were ingeniously organised by mothers when Nancy would be in attendance. One family called Casserley was a particular concern. The mother was a widow in poor circumstances with a family of eight, the eldest of whom, Ricky, aged twelve, was an endearing honest boy and a favourite with Nancy.

The years passed and she became popular in the community. During evenings off she got involved in the simple pranks and affairs that relieve the boredom of a deprived society. She attended local functions, concerts and dances. At times she had what were regarded as steady boyfriends but the relationships petered out, mainly because she was somewhat choosy and, as people said, not inclined to settle down. All that changed, however, when she was swept off her feet at a house dance by Jamesy Fitzhenry and a liaison resulted which was of a passionate order until she horrifyingly found herself pregnant. When she broached the matter with Jamesy his amorous attitude hardened and he disappeared out of her life for nearly two months.

Eventually, she enlisted her friend, Brigid Mulholland, who worked with her as a nanny in O'Raleighs, to confront him on her behalf. Brigid was made of stern stuff and pulled no punches.

"You are responsible," she told him "and if you're a man at all you'll marry her. Do you want her to face sacking and disgrace? If you travelled the length of Ireland you wouldn't find a more decent woman. Will I tell her you'll agree to marry her?"

But the news that Brigid brought back was agonising. Nancy's high spirits were shattered. She was terrified.

"There's only one thing for it," Brigid advised her. "See Fr Glennon, in the name of God. If there's anyone can make him do the right thing it's Fr Glennon. I'll go with you and wait outside the parochial house. Tomorrow evening will be a good time to go and please God you'll get things sorted out."

Time and options were running out for Nancy. Her free, independent spirit was undermined. She felt guilty and abject that she had let down her religion, her family and her employer. To some extent, her maternal instincts sustained her but without the comfort and advice of her true friend, Brigid, she would have been unable even to think coherently. Anything that Brigid suggested was explored and, consequently, after tea on the following evening, both women walked together in the early January night to the parochial house about a mile distant.

There had been a spell of heavy frost and the night was bitterly cold. A full moon shone in a cloudless sky of twinkling stars. Creaking sounds in the high branches of the huge trees around the parochial house intermittently grated on the eerie stillness. Through the trees, dim lights profiled the curtained windows in the ivied walls. Nancy walked nervously along the grassy edge of the pebbled driveway.

"I'll keep praying for you," Brigid assured her.

The housekeeper, Lena Cowley, answered the door and led Nancy into a room off the hallway. There was a lighted paraffin lamp on the table and a log fire in the grate.

"Take a seat," Lena directed, drawing one of the high padded chairs anglewise from the table. "Fr Glennon will be with you in a few minutes."

Nancy, sitting bolt upright with a handbag on her knees, felt it was an eternity before she heard deadened footsteps on the stairs and Fr Glennon surged into the room.

"Oh," he exclaimed in an unexpectedly kindly tone, "you're the housekeeper with the O'Raleighs. What can I do for you, my child?"

"I'm in trouble, Father," she blurted out, with deep feelings of disgust and mental pain.

The priest dealt with her movingly. She had agreed to meet him as Brigid had suggested because he had a reputation for dealing with recalcitrant philanderers as well as other miscreants. He preached fiery and frightening sermons and was severe at confessions. She had expected that he would lecture and upbraid her, that he would want details of all her sins. In nervous mood and broken sentences she told her story and entreated him to compel Jamesy Fitzhenry to marry her. His only questions related to reassurance that he was the man responsible.

"Father," she said when the interview was ending, "if he doesn't marry me I feel like doing away with myself."

Clearly upset, he looked into her eyes with tenderness and compassion, the antithesis of the terrifying zealot.

"Pray, my child. Have faith," he said softly. "I'll do my best with the help of God."

She was leaving and he was about to close the door behind her when, encouraged by the priest's understanding and compassion, she turned abruptly and edged back into the hall.

"Father," she pleaded, "won't you make him marry me!"

He was visibly affected. With all his experience and training, with his normally cold exterior and distinction for severity, there was an inner core of kindness and pity that could not be subdued or concealed. There was a long pause. His lips twitched and he squeezed his fingers tightly together.

"Yes, my child," he replied. "I'll see that he shoulders his responsibility as a Christian."

Nancy rejoined her friend, Brigid, with a lighter heart than she had known for a very long time.

Marcus Clerkin arrived in the Morris Cowley at Geblik church before three o'clock and saw nobody around. He strolled inside and, to his surprise, found Fr Glennon kneeling in a seat near the altar. The priest seemed to be lost in prayer or reverie, with his elbows resting on the top rail of the seat in front of him and his face cast downwards in cupped hands. Marcus coughed, pulled at a seat and scraped the floor with his feet to attract his attention but to no avail. Finally, he walked up the aisle and gently touched the priest's shoulder. Fr Glennon reacted with a momentary quiver, then straightened, genuflected in front of the tabernacle and followed Marcus out of the church.

"I'm ready now, Father, if you want to go to the Cushogs to see Jamesy Fitzhenry," he told the priest.

"Thank you, my child, thank you," Fr Glennon intoned distraitly as he climbed into the rear seat of the car.

It took less than half an hour to reach their destination and not a word was spoken until they got there. Fr Glennon was not a loquacious man at any time. He generally communicated in a perfunctory kind of way that seemed part of his pernickety, aloof nature. During this drive he restrained himself to the occasional extended nasal groan, which was his habit, that gave the impression of a safety valve reacting to a build-up in emotional stress or pressure. He respired through pursed lips and continuously fidgeted with his hands, rubbing them together or twirling one thumb around the other. The normal ruddy freshness in his puffed face had paled and there was a tinge of blue in his lips and cheeks. In all his associations with the priest, sober or in various stages of inebriation, Marcus had experienced an incongruity, a remoteness from the constraints of the real world.

But he had never seen him so tensed and apprehensive before.

"I see them," Marcus exclaimed, pointing to a group of three men working on the side of a drain a few hundred yards across the rushy field. "If you hang on here, Father, I'll tell Jamesy Fitzhenry you want him."

"Thank you," Fr Glennon replied, getting out of the car and pulling the large black hat tightly down on his forehead.

Marcus leapt over a decrepit wooden gate and walked along a furzy ditch. A herd of cattle frightened by the strange sight and noise of the car scampered wildly through the field before returning to gaze cautiously at the unusual spectacle, then suddenly took off again to repeat the exercise. The men were alert to the situation since the sound of the approaching car was heard in the distance, but they continued to work with feigned unawareness until Marcus landed close beside them.

"How's the men?" he inquired in greeting. "A good job you're doin' there!"

Jamesy Fitzhenry was in his shirt sleeves working a drag near the bottom of the bank.

"Have you a few minutes to spare, Pontius," Marcus asked, using the epithet lately applied to him. "The Canon wants to have a few words with you."

Marcus was conscious of Jamesy's reputation as an irascible and unpredictable firebrand, and he realised from the start the difficulty of Fr Glennon's mission. Tough men had failed to tame Fitzhenry, and few would consider that an ageing, ingenuous curate could discipline or manage him. Marcus would not have been surprised if Jamesy had ordered him to get the priest out of his sight directly. But he was aware from experience that Fr Glennon had a habit of springing surprises, even in the most adverse circumstances. What amazed him was Jamesy's genial, carefree attitude.

"Certainly," he responded. "I'll do whatever I can to help any priest that has a problem."

His two fellow workers, Prick McGinnity and Micksheen the Blackguard, moved to the top of the bank and, along with Marcus, watched intently with an affected casualness as Jamesy stroked a few heavy blobs of clay on the front of his patched trousers and pulled suspended galluses across his shoulders. Then he tightened loose whangs on worn-out hobnailed boots, and, whistling a soft tune, strode nonchalantly towards the road. The excited cattle continued to jostle noisily around, a flock of crows flew overhead and two hares ran across the headland.

"The hares'd talk to ye around here, Father," Jamesy remarked, in an attempt to set a tone of relief to the tautness of the occasion.

Fr Glennon, oozing with indignation, portly and urbane, impeccably dressed in black clerical garb with assertive mien, bulging eyes and tightly clasped hands, the epitome of propriety and authority, faced the wild, beragged and erratic philanderer and remained silent with a fixed, accusing stare. It is unlikely that memories of their previous encounter, when Jamesy victoriously subverted his Passion sermon at Holmogats, did not cross the priest's mind.

"Can I do anything for you, Father?" Jamesy inquired casually.

"No," Fr Glennon retorted coldly, "you can't. I wouldn't personally ask your help. But you could do a lot for Nancy Mulligan. And you could do a lot for Christ by living up to your religion, to your responsibilities."

"I suppose I could, Father, and I know you have your job to do, but I have my mind made up. I knew well what you were coming for, I'm not denying, but you're only wasting your time."

Fr Glennon lost his composure.

"You impudent cur!" he raged. "By God I'll show you whether or not I'm wasting my time. If you don't change your tune I'll denounce you from the altar. Do you admit responsibility? Are you the father of this woman's child?"

"That's what I couldn't say for sure, Father."

"What the fecking hell do you mean, you bastard? Did you have sexual intercourse with this woman?"

"There could be other Jack Horners that put in their thumbs, Father."

The priest gyrated and fulminated in anger at the effrontery and nonchalance of the impenitent profligate.

"Listen, you hoor," he roared, "you're a proper bowsie! I'll see that you get married!"

"Well actually, Father, I was planning to get married all right, but to another woman, Mary Slevin. As a matter of fact I was thinking of calling on you soon to arrange the wedding."

"Mary Slevin!" Fr Glennon repeated loudly in disbelief. "Are you talking of the decent girl that arranges flowers for the altar?"

"That's right, Father, she's very tasty with flowers and things like that."

"Well, by God, her taste is not up to much in other ways! And you are not free to marry her, you have a serious obligation to marry the woman you made pregnant, Nancy Mulligan."

"I'm telling you, Father, I have no intention of marrying her. I have nothing against her but that's the way it is."

This declaration left no room for doubt regarding Jamesy's disposition. Fr Glennon's aggressive deportment vacillated, then crumpled like a punctured balloon. The glaring hopelessness of his mission disconcerted him. Although in many ways ill-equipped for his calling, he had a nobility of soul that impelled him. Emotionally, he was bonded irrevocably to those he sought to serve; their problems brought him nights of sleeplessness and mental anguish. While his intentions and commitment were beyond question, his manner was brusque and wayward; he was like a poor swimmer lashing bravely but futilely to save shipwrecked victims in a turbulent sea. Leaning a hand against the bonnet of the car for support, and with glazed eyes fixed in a mystical stare, he spoke abstractedly in soliloquy.

"Jesus, Mary and Joseph," he intoned. "I can understand human frailty and sins of the flesh. They are committed in passing moments and are repented. But a man who deliberately ruins a woman's life for his own pleasure, who spurns his own flesh and blood and shirks his responsibility, who condemns his child to perdition and shame, is a vile reprobate unworthy to be called a Christian. Even brute animals have nature in them."

Now, Jamesy Fitzhenry was not the totally inflexible character that his demeanour projected. He was fiery, independent and volatile. But the hard image was essentially a cover for feelings of inadequacy and immaturity. Essentially, he had an amenable ad hoc regard for fairness and moral probity, and his nature constantly strained on the curbs imposed by the ethos of social convention. Some of his friends had urged him to marry Nancy Mulligan. A few concerned members of the community made plain their views that she was too good for him. Nobody had a wrong word to say about her. Only one associate, who had himself left a woman in the lurch, claimed that the paternity issue in such cases was seldom straightforward; as the old saying went, a hen that lays outside the nest once can never be trusted! But Jamesy's perspective on mating responsibility did not include faithfulness to one partner either, and there were quite a few who were amazed that his run of luck had lasted so long. Nevertheless, Fr Glennon's introspective musings had disconcerted him. Besides, his confused conscience had niggled at him in a way that was becoming more uncomfortable. Above all, while an indifferent believer and churchgoer, like the preponderance of parishioners, his respect for the clergy was unconditional. He could be, and invariably was, impertinent and impossible to varying degrees, but he shared an ingrained religious conviction that was sacrosanct and precious.

There was another concern that increasingly disconcerted him: the consequences which his stance entailed for his own mother, as well as for Nancy Mulligan's mother, played on his mind.

Brigid Fitzhenry had experienced life's harrowing sorrows. She endured them with courage and equanimity, with true Christian fortitude. Through all the years of misfortune she hoped and prayed. Less resolute souls would have wilted in despair. There was a toughness, almost a coarseness, in her character that daunted most people. But it was a façade. While outwardly uncivil and abrasive, inwardly she was sensitive and at peace. Always attentive to her religious duties she recited the rosary nightly. In a small brown paper parcel hanging from the loft she stored the Franciscan habit, the garb she would wear at her waking. When she heard of Jamesy's transgression she reprimanded him severely and implored him to marry Nancy Mulligan if he was responsible for the pregnancy. He knew that, apart from religious conviction, the situation was a humiliation for her in the community. As the days passed he noticed a worrying paleness in her features and frustration in her manner as she rebuked and entreated him incessantly. Although the relationship had always been stiff and strained he had a respect and a concern for her. In spite of his tough and obstinate nature the situation was for him a cause of misgiving and anxiety.

Accounts had also been relayed to Jamesy of the pain and distress which Nancy's mother, Margie, was enduring. She was a kind and simple soul that was loved and respected in the community. Her son, Hubert, Nancy's elder and only brother, was also pained and shattered. Jamesy had felt a growing sense of unhappiness as the agent of such agony.

A myriad of thoughts crowded his brain and overwhelmed him as he listened to the priest's impassioned invocations. Feelings akin to those of a checkmated mountaineer, unable to reach the daunting summit at the top but with a lifeline to a lower, safe though unchallenging, plateau, began to affect him. He wilted, a seemingly irrational gesture which was a feature of his character.

"Father," he said reverentially, "give me a while to think about it."

The softened reaction took the priest by surprise. He realised the tide had turned and the punctured ego was triggered to inflate again.

"Yes, James," he replied in a firm but more relaxed tone, "you will get plenty of time to think about it, for the rest of your life. But what I want from you now is a commitment that you will marry Nancy Mulligan."

"Marry her, Father? Marry her when?"

"This day fortnight in Geblik Church."

"Ah, for Christ's sake, Father! That's too soon. How on earth could a wedding be arranged, the ring and everything else, in two weeks?"

"It's nearly a year too late, son. And I have arranged weddings at a day's notice. What I want you to do is to meet me in the parochial house tomorrow night with Miss Mulligan at eight o'clock. Tell her about the arrangement. We will go into all the details then."

"All right, Father, if that's what ye want," Jamesy replied respectfully, with a pronounced shrug of acquiescence and resignation.

*

Prick McGinnity and Micksheen the Blackguard had kept moving haphazardly on the bank of the drain while Jamesy made his way to the priest at the roadway. Marcus remained with them, making the odd humdrum observation. All kept the confrontation in the distance under observation, although the proceedings were mostly out of earshot. Some words were clearly heard though, including references to Mary Slevin.

"Isn't the Canon a very simple man to believe he could lay down the law for Pontius," Prick remarked with the air of an authority on the obduracy of human nature.

"Well, begod," agreed Micksheen, "wouldn't ye think he'd have the gumption to know when he's up agin a thoroughbred mule. Pontius is not man enough to admit his mistakes and pay the price for them. That's the end of it."

"There is only one way ye might manage him," claimed the Prick. "If you wanted him to go left bid him to go right. He'd try to prove that black is white! If he says it's a fine day, agree with him – even if it's lashin' rain!"

"I wouldn't be too sure that Fr Glennon is not a match for him," Marcus observed with some sense of team loyalty. "He's no pushover for anybody, I can tell ye."

"Hasn't an earthly," claimed the Prick.

"Wasting his time," agreed the Blackguard.

"Here," challenged Marcus, somewhat peeved at the lopsided and superficial assessment, "I'll bet a bob Fr Glennon gets his way, that he'll make Pontius marry Nancy Mulligan. Will ye cover it with a tanner apiece?"

The bet was agreed and tension mounted as time moved on and there was no indication as to the outcome. Finally, they noted Pontius moving away from the scene, vaulting over the wooden gate and returning along the hedgerow. Marcus started to move towards the roadway and slowed briefly when they met.

"Well," he inquired under his breath, "how did you get on?"

"Ah," Jamesy replied, "you might as well try to shift a jack ass. He's making me marry her. What the hell about it, anyway."

"You're doing the right thing, lad," Marcus assured him as they both kept moving.

"Well," Prick wanted to know, how did it go?"

"Bad," Pontius answered walking past.

"How do you mean bad?" Prick shouted after him.

"He's making me marry her. There's nothing I can feckin' well do about it!"

Prick was speechless and looked gapingly at the Blackguard who in turn was dumbfounded and extremely distressed at the loss of his sixpence.

"The fuckin' cowardly cunt," he blurted, nodding malevolently in the direction of the ambling Pontius. "He's not man enough to stand his ground when it's put up to him!"

*

News that Pontius Pilate had been harpooned by the Canon spread through the parish like wildfire. There were several accounts of the circumstances. According to one reliable source the priest had grabbed the delinquent by the throat and, lifting him off the ground, shook him violently until the choking malcontent signified acquiescence. An equally impeccable source claimed the curate had paralysed him with his priestly power and only liberated him when Pontius agreed to fulfil his obligations and marry Nancy Mulligan.

All accounts recognised the pivotal role Fr Glennon had played in sorting out the misfortune. In general, there was agreement that justice was prevailing; Nancy Mulligan was a decent, respectable girseach and it would be a sin if she were humiliated and devastated. Others felt it was a sin that her life should be ruined by getting tied to an unmanageable rapscallion. There were those with mixed feelings who considered she was no chicken; at twenty-nine years of age she should have more sense. But to the vast majority of people in the wider community, whatever happened was a matter of minor and passing concern, even callous jokes.

The wedding was solemnised outside the altar by Fr Glennon at eight o'clock mass on a cold Wednesday morning. Pontius Pilate was impressively groomed and Nancy Mulligan looked radiant in an over-sized brown breasted suit. Brigid Mulholland was bridesmaid and John Dowey best man. Ricky Casserly served the mass. There was a substantial attendance of friends at the ceremony, the main participants and relations travelling by horse-drawn traps, others on bicycles or on foot.

After mass the group waited outside the main door of the church and as the married couple emerged light snowflakes wafted in the air around them. Marcus Clerkin, who happened to be in the vicinity of the church at the time, felt it was a pity there was no photographer to capture the scene, the happy couple ducking through snowflakes and handfuls of oaten meal.

The reception was held in the bride's house and was acclaimed a joyous and memorable occasion. Even the groom's mother,

Brigid, entered into the spirit of the event. There was music on accordion, concertina and fiddle, with dancing and singing. Two half-barrels of porter, whiskey, tea and stacks of food, including two dozen stewed rabbits provided as presents, ensured that the function had a matchless rating on the complex but reliable shitometer scale for areas bereft of sanitary facilities.

There is no photograph to show any feature of the happy occasion, and nothing logged that would build up a picture of conditions and emotions. All that is recorded in the parish register are the stark salient facts: Jamesy Fitzhenry, a farm labourer aged twenty-five years, married Anne Mulligan, spinster and domestic servant aged twenty-nine years, on the last Wednesday of January, 1929.

*

Two weeks after the wedding, Marcus Clerkin got an urgent message late at night from the priests' housekeeper, Lena Cowley, to attend at the parochial house. He got there to discover that Fr Glennon was extremely inebriated. From her barricaded position in the kitchen, Lena explained the situation to him.

"He's drinking all day from shortly after breakfast. I never saw him as bad. Whatever came over him I don't know but he's in a terrible state!"

"Did anyone cross him or say anything annoying to him?" Marcus asked.

"No," Lena replied. "There was nobody around all day but myself."

"And did you say anything upsetting to him?"

"No, not a thing. I just told him the story that's going around, that Mary Slevin took the boat to England 'cause she's in trouble.

I did say it'll be hard to get anyone to do flowers on the altar like her – sure that could hardly drive him to the drink, would you say?"

"How is anyone to know?" Marcus responded evasively in a pensive and subdued mood. "Only the man above could tell. I wouldn't have any opinion on that," he lied, unsavoury images of Pontius playing on his distraught mind.

"Might it be the child that he's thinking of?"

"The bastard!" Marcus intoned abstractedly under his breath, alluding to Pilate the wrongdoer.

"Oh, Jesus, Mary and Joseph," Lena protested, "how could anyone be so cruel?"

Marcus shrugged a shoulder, thinking she was referring to Pontius Pilate.

Predestined To Be A Millionaire

Prologue

Change crawled charily, convulsively, comprehensively. For many people, times were improving, for others conditions were static if not regressive. Progress is seldom constant, it is marked with recoils and inconsistencies. There was wealth and poverty, health and sickness, hope and despondency, happiness and sadness, success and failure, enlightenment and ignorance. Mostly ignorance, naivety, simpleness.

There were ghosts and haunted houses and fairies. Ghosts were seen only at night, they faded into the light of day. The evil and troubled spirits in haunted houses only appeared after dark. Terrifying stories were told around the fires at night with the latest exposé of the unsettled supernatural miscreants. Even though the petrifying accounts were mostly related at secondhand, and by narrators whose reputations were sustained on imagination and hyperbole, their effects could be regarded as analogous to sacramental: they made an indelible mark on the soul, a debilitating scar never to be effaced.

Ghosts and haunted houses had their positive aspects, though. Security was one consideration; it would take a particularly intrepid rogue to enter at night a place that featured in eerie stories. A doctor who lived in a bleak mansion at the end of a long, gloomy, tree-lined avenue made it known that he witnessed baleful ghosts regularly; he never got any calls for his professional services after dark!

Fairies, or the little people, as they were sometimes called, unlike ghosts, were real, a type of miniature human being with magical powers. They resided out of sight in caves or mottes where they had crocks of gold hidden. A large group of fairies resided in the Motte of Geblik and was seen for brief periods now and again. Generally, fairies were harmless and inoffensive, but a band of them bate the shite out of Paddy Gibney when he strayed on to their path in broad daylight crossing the *Lios*, an expansive undulating field. Straying onto a fairy path was a dreaded, though not an unusual, occurrence; it could happen whenever a man crossed a large, lonesome field. As a result, the individual became confused and could not find a way out. The solution was for him to turn his coat inside out and wear it that way until he got his bearings.

There were occasional unusual sightings of fairies. They were seen a few times playing a game of football in the Crockan. Brigid Fitzhenry as a young girl witnessed Garret Gearlog's regiment marching across the Ho-Boy stile towards Elgravstown Castle early on a sunny summer morning. The liveried soldiers were about eighteen inches tall.

*

For the majority of people, survival was the dominant problem. Although everything is relative, there is a bottom line and the gauge was moving very sluggishly near the base. Poverty was widespread. Employment was sporadic. Hunger and malnutrition were rife. Ills and disease ranged from boils and sores to deadly consumption. Many people dressed poorly in patched or tattered clothes; in some cases, where parents and siblings shared the same clothes, members of families had to attend masses at different times.

For large numbers emigration was the only saviour. Many young people left in an unbecoming hurry that caused suspicions and stories. Some who were pushed to the edge turned to tramping and begging, many of them, to salvage some pride, under the guise of providing a service, such as selling small items, fortune-telling or playing the bones or comb. Tinkers tried to eke out an existence by making or mending buckets, pots and cans, charging a trifle for work of extraordinary artistry and skill. If they remained a few days camped with the caravans and horses in one place, residents complained and the police moved them on unceremoniously.

Circuses and shows came occasionally and performed in pitched canvas tents on the village green. They brought a carnival atmosphere about the place, but a small group of mature louts nearly always spoiled the occasion with their own brand of entertainment, clodding and disrupting the proceedings.

Housing was poor but improving. Some families still kept animals and fowl in their dwellings. Thatched roofs that were poorly maintained leaked during rainfall; pots and other utensils strategically placed on the floor collected most of the dribbles, but in extreme cases families had to seek shelter outside. During storms thatched roofs were particularly vulnerable and safeguarding them was a communal effort. Men – and sometimes women – yelled orders and hung desperately on ropes in struggles with hurricane-force winds. When the storms died down success would be celebrated. But sometimes the endeavours were in vain.

There was always the quest for land. Progress had been made, ranches had been broken up and the Irish Land Commission was in the process of allotting farms and building houses. Cottages had been built for farm labourers and more were programmed.

In sport, Gaelic football attracted widespread support but there were other popular activities including cycling, tug-o-war, athletics and camogie. Hurling never took hold in Geblik. A match was held in the early days between two outside teams in an effort to popularise the sport. An elderly gentleman left the scene unimpressed and afterwards referred to the match as a dangerous game of football played with sticks.

Religion vied with superstitions, fairy tales and quackery as a motivating influence. In the resultant mishmash there were amalgams and overlaps. Numbers seemed to be of great significance for all of them, threes, sevens and tens having great importance.

Dancing was the craze for the young and those not so young. House dances were widespread but considered particularly pernicious by Church and State. A bill to control public dancing would shortly be passed by the Dáil.

Other diversions included pitch and toss banks on Sundays and summer evenings, and halfpenny in the twenty-five card games on winter nights. Coursing, fishing and poaching were also indulged in, as well as bird catching – mostly goldfinch.

Politics was a divisive subject and in Geblik there was a strong Fianna Fáil majority. Éamon de Valera, leader of the new party, was regarded as a messiah by his myriad supporters who acted heavy-handedly with the opposition during the general election campaigns of February, 1932, and January, 1933. The results of these elections set Fianna Fáil on a power course that was a cause of concern to serious thinkers. For many poor and labouring families, de Valera's success represented a final victory, entry to the Promised Land. For others it was perdition.

The year 1932 was marked by events that had serious repercussions for even the most remote corners of Geblik parish. In June, the Eucharistic Congress was held to mark the 1,500th anniversary of St Patrick's return to Ireland to preach Christianity; the Blueshirt movement emerged and the Economic War started in earnest.

End of Prologue

Thomas Farrell was generally addressed as Tomboy but referred to in the third person as the Twit. He was a young bachelor who lived alone in a small, dilapidated thatched cottage on about five acres of land. Not a man to lather a sweat working, he got infrequent spells with the county council as a roadworker or breaking stones in the nearby quarry. Apart from that he occasionally got a few days employment with farmers during busy periods. Nearly six feet tall and somewhat gaunt he dressed indifferently, often with rumpled clothes buttoned or pinned askew, and boots laced with twine. A slight rigidity in the neck and shoulder movements was evident whenever he decided to bestir himself. There was a gaucheness and reticence about him, as well as a clumsiness in communication, that marked him as an inoffensive, half-witted loner.

At school, although it had been impossible to teach him anything, he passed yearly from class to class because there was no facility to give him the specialist attention he obviously required. He was a daydreamer who could not concentrate on the work at hand. The teacher claimed he was wired to the moon – if a bird flew by the window his interest and excitement would discommode the whole class. Strangely enough, at a glance he could tell the breed of every bird. Formal learning, though, was beyond his capability. So he drifted with the group as a decided bother to the teacher but very often a source of light relief and jollity to his classmates.

At Irish classes he had two stock replies to all questions in his native tongue: *tá* and *níl*. He also developed a defensive guard that any prizefighter would envy; no matter how many vicious punches the teacher aimed at his head he took them on deft arms and elbows. When the teacher, ominously hovering close to his seat, asked a question *as gaeilge,* Tomboy immediately switched into a cowering, protective mode and ventured a *tá* through quivering arms. Depending on the look on the teacher's face, he could tighten defences and do an instantaneous about-turn with a burst of *níls*.

When he finished at the national school, in sixth class and aged fourteen, his educational development was abysmally limited. Any competence he had was confined to English composition, where his efforts were invariably brief, offbeat and regularly whimsical. A couple of weeks before the school closed for the summer holidays in his final year, the homework set was an essay on *Our Cat.* Tomboy's dissertation was typical of his unusual creative talent.

The teacher's normal procedure was to read out all the essays to the class, standing close to the desk of the pupil concerned. He would start off with the composition considered the best and work downwards to the poorest. All the good points would be emphasised, poor presentation criticised and mistakes corrected.

There were many interesting references to the feline condition made in the compositions – evolution and domestication, breeds, problems and usefulness, colours and various other intriguing aspects. Finally, the teacher reached the last copy, penned by Tomboy, and moved close to his desk. As usual, the endangered pupil's defence mechanism switched to autopilot.

"Now," the teacher announced to the amused class, "we come to a writer with a talent in the mould of Charles Dickens, a really deep thinker with a unique and effective manner of expression. A boy destined to surprise the world and go places!"

There were pupils in the class who would recall those prophetic words in years to come.

"The modernised syntax is very striking," continued the teacher, "as well as the simplified spelling."

Then he set about the onerous task of orally doing justice to the esoteric lines in the grubby copybook:

our kat we hav a kat a tome, she is a buk sum kats kum atipin udders don't buk kats ate kittens if they get a chanc a kat has nyn lives I belev theres a bred of kat whot has nyn tales and a nudder bred has no tale atal kats always kum on ther feat when they fal they say sum kats ware pidgamas a fella told me wunce I was a cats paw howsever he maid that out they say kats is sum way related to banshes a blak kat is lukie cats is very musikal bekos ther guts is used in fidels kats bery ther durt but ther pis is very smelie a kat has sharp klaws when he is fritened and can giv an oful skrape buk kats are bad raters dogs are tru frends but a starvin kat wud ate a ded owner if they wer loked in a hous, a kat shud not be let out ov the bag wher ther is pidgins thers a tipe of english kat whot lafs sum pepel klame that kats kan sea in the dark beter than in the lite but they kanot see as gud as pigs bekose pigs kan sea the wind.

All of the pupils found the observations extremely hilarious with an originality of slant which was a hallmark of Tomboy's outlook. There was a subdued look of concern as well as amusement in the teacher's eyes as he set about analysing and educationally milking the curious reflections.

"Thomas," he began, "there's a very fine line dividing the genius from the fool. Does it tell you anything if I confirm that sometimes – very, very occasionally – I have difficulty in deciding on which side of the line you are located?"

"Oh, yes, it does, sir! It tells me a lot, sir!"

"And what, may I ask, is the gist of what it tells you?"

"It tells me, sir, that you're not as clever as people think!"

The teacher kept his cool with a special effort on account of the occasion, warned the class to behave themselves, and turned his eyes again to the scrawled writing in the tousled manuscript.

"Your spelling and grammar are atrocious, beyond remedy at this stage without doubt. But let us consider just one of the daft points you make. Is there anyone else in the class that believes tom cats eat kittens?"

All the children put up their hands.

"I see," mused the teacher. "Well, you will all be finishing school shortly and moving out to work in the real world. And in the real world male cats do not eat their offspring any more than other animals, with the possible exception of sow pigs. What happens in the real world is that the numbers of cats have to be kept under control. Your parents have to get rid of kittens and they do so mostly by drowning them. Drowning, of course, is cruel, but to allow numbers to increase without control would be much more cruel and unacceptable. Children who do not understand the ways of the world would be horrified to know that beautiful and innocent kittens are got rid of in this way. So parents tell them that the drowned kittens were eaten by tom cats. It's what's called a white lie."

Some of the pupils were noticeably disconcerted with this information and the teacher measured the reaction by running his eyes around the class.

"In the real world you are mainly left to your own resources and must face facts. By the way," he added as an afterthought, "how many of you believe in Santa Claus?"

Tomboy was the only child to raise a hand. "All right, all right," the teacher continued, turning to him. "Your composition combines a commendable perceptiveness with a disquieting ignorance. There's nothing I can do about it at this stage. God knows I tried hard enough through the years. You brought me pain and tribulation and I have no doubt you will bring the same to many others who may try to help you. I am not blaming you, mind, just making a point. You are a hostage to fortune! Do you understand?"

"Yes, sir," Tomboy responded with unconcealed glee, completely misconstruing the remark. He fantasised often about becoming involved in wealth and fame and the mention of fortune excited him. Little did he know that in such a context the teacher's observations manifested remarkable prescience.

*

Agnes McDunphy, generally referred to as Aggy, lived in Lectastown, an adjoining parish to Geblik. In 1932, in her forty-sixth year, she met and became friendly with Tomboy Farrell, who was then twenty-four years old. The whole parish was enthralled and mesmerised by the relationship and there were various stories regarding its origin, mostly of a sordid nature and many of them a test for the wildest imagination.

Aggy was neither bright nor educated but, as some people put it, she was crafty in her own way. She was about five foot six inches tall and her long, curly, auburn hair had streaks of grey. Prick McGinnity, who had a good feel for an animal, had mixed views about her.

"Well," he pontificated, "we can't accuse her of bein' good

lookin'. Not a lot between the ears, either. A bit heavy of the diddies an' light of the arse. But not a bad oul' stripper at all, though!"

After she finished school Aggy had worked for several years with local farmers. Her early years in service had their setbacks. At the start of her first job the farmer's wife told her that breakfast would be at eight o'clock in the morning. Aggy understood that breakfast would be served or brought to her at eight so she asked the lady to call her if she were asleep. In the next job, the family went on holidays for two weeks and Aggy was left in charge. She did no work whatsoever and when the family returned they were horrified. The lady went to accost Aggy in her room, which was also topsy-turvy. When asked the reason for all the cobwebs, Aggy blamed the bloody spiders! In yet another job she was sacked for incompetence, the farmer's wife claiming she didn't even know how to try a hen, a basic skill for any servant girl working for a farmer. In due time, however, she was shaped into an automaton programmed to serve proficiently and without the handicap of a distinct intelligence.

She then went to Dublin where she was employed in the one house for over fifteen years. When she returned there were rumours that she had got into difficulties in her employment, but nobody knew for certain what had happened. Since then she had kept mostly to herself, and had no close friends or relatives. She lived frugally but dressed well and never seemed to be in want. For all her faults and failings there was a certain aura of respectability, even superciliousness, about her.

It was evident before long that Aggy and Tomboy were a permanent twosome, despite the age differential. Clearly, Aggy was the instigator of the affair because Tomboy was reclusive, diffident and docile, whereas Aggy was resolute and strong-willed. Some were unkind enough to claim, with regard to her age, that desperation was the motivation. According to another rumour, when she got the whimper of Tomboy's daydreaming that he would be falling in for a fortune, she was captivated by it.

"Since I was at school," he confirmed to her, "I'm all the time expectin' to fall in for a fortune. The teacher, whatever he knew, gave me the tip-off. I have a notion it's goin' to happen soon."

"God, I hope you're right," she told him. "Where do you expect it to come from?"

"I haven't a notion," he replied. "But there were close relations went to America after the famine and they were supposed to do very well for themselves, so they were."

"You never can tell, can you?" she retorted. "We'll hold on for a while and give a chance to your hunch. I'll talk to someone I know about it. Strange things can happen."

She was right. About three months afterwards she was cooking dinner in her home when a wrought-up Tomboy burst through the door.

"We're made up, we're made up," he declared, excitedly waving an envelope. "When I got the letter this mornin' I went down to Monitor Crawley to read it and he tells me we're made up! There it's for ye! Whoever ye talked to must have done somethin'."

She took the envelope and pulled out the letter, standing with her back to the table. It was from a law attorney in New York and addressed to Thomas Farrell, Esquire. The information was brief and tenuous, but encouraging:

This is to confirm that we are pressing your claim to be the lawful beneficiary of the Farrell fortune of several million dollars left by Timothy Farrell, a bachelor, who died intestate. At this stage we only wish to say that from the information provided to us your case appears to be clear-cut. In order to help us bring the matter to a satisfactory conclusion at the earliest possible time I would request you to call personally to the offices of the Honourable Fredrick A. Stirling, United States Ambassador to Ireland, at the American Legation in Ireland, Phoenix Park, Dublin, to have the attached form countersigned and returned to us. Make sure to ask for and deal with Pedro McPartlin, who is only available to the public on the last Friday of every month. We would hope to be in contact with you shortly afterwards regarding the situation. As a gesture of your endorsement to proceed please let us have a remittance of two-hundred dollars with your reply. Respond only through Pedro McPartlin, Esq., at the American Legation in Ireland.

Aggy was cool as well as cute.

"It's very good news all right," she said. "I'm not too sure we're made up just yet though. But I'll keep in touch with my source and we might know more soon enough. We'll manage the two-hundred dollars. Keep it under your hat for a while until I get this advice."

Tomboy was somewhat disappointed at this down-to-earth response but he was prepared to abide by Aggy's better judgement. In any event, time was never a great worry to him. However, later that evening he was to learn that the story was a matter of public knowledge and already out of control. When he arrived home there was a large hackney car at the gate and as he got off his bicycle the driver, John Sheerman, jumped out of the vehicle.

"I believe congratulations are in order regarding the good news," he began, giving a warm handshake to a surprised Tomboy with one hand and patting him on the shoulder with the other.

"Well, I suppose, in a way, more or less, maybe," Tomboy spluttered, realising that the reference was to the letter about his fortune, but puzzled to understand how the affair had become public in a matter of hours when such a development had never entered his head.

"I believe you got a welcome letter this morning that puts the charge in your corner. Well, if I can do anything..."

"Begod, that's very good of ye. Aye, I did, I got a letter all right," Tomboy replied. "Here it is," he continued, pulling it out of his pocket after a momentary pause.

John Sheerman read and re-read the letter.

"We'll have to attend to this, sonny," he stated. "We'll have to attend to it without delay. This is too important to put on the long finger."

"That's what I thought meself," Tomboy agreed, "although there's others think we should let it take its time. But, anyway, I'm just not in a position to deal with it right now."

"Nonsense, sonny," retorted John Sheerman. "That's what friends are for, to help out when they're wanted. I'm here to help you out with this, if you'll allow me."

"I know you mean well, Mr Sheerman," Tomboy acknowledged to the benevolent gentleman that he had never spoken to before in his life, "but I'm in no position to get to the Phoenix Park or to pay two-hundred dollars at the present time."

"Now, now, sonny, don't call me mister, my name is John. I'll see you're in a position to do both. Tomorrow is the last Friday in the month, are you free in the morning?"

"Well, I am, sure there's no work at present as ye know yerself."

"Be ready at nine in the morning, sonny, and I'll collect you here."

"Well, begod, Mister... er... John, that's very dacent of ye! I will in troth, I'll be waitin' for ye. An' a thousand thanks to ye. I hope I'll be able to make it up to ye, so I do."

*

John Sheerman was the proprietor of a thriving garage business in the town of Skell. There was a staff of seven or eight mechanics and four or five other employees. Apart from selling and mending cars, motorbikes and bicycles, other machinery was handled on the premises. Additional lines included wireless sets, gramophones and records. A very successful hackney service was also conducted from the centre. John himself was a shrewd businessman, generally affable and witty but caustic and blunt on occasions. Once he was hired to drive a lady home from Skell to Geblik when Fr Drake called to his shop and offered her a lift in his trap. She cancelled the arrangement much to John's annoyance that the priest would interfere with his business. Looking Fr Drake in the eye, he offered to say mass for him the next Sunday morning.

"If you take the bit out of my mouth, I'll do the same for you."

John happened to be in the showroom on this particular Thursday shortly after lunch when Monitor Crawley called to enquire about a second-hand bicycle. Monitor was so called because he had filled that role in his final year at the national school. He was considered a fountain of learning and knowledge.

"Go on outta that with you, sonny," John teased him. "Put your hand down in your pocket and buy a new Raleigh. Money is no problem to you."

"Well I'll tell ye one thing," Monitor declared, "I met a man a couple of hours ago that hasn't a tosser but before long he'll be fit to buy the whole town of Skell!"

John's entrepreneurial antennae elevated. He invited Monitor into his office where he listened attentively to the full story.

"There's not a doubt in the world about it," Monitor declared. "He's goin' to be a millionaire!"

"That's a fret, sonny," John proclaimed. "If it was another man that told me I wouldn't believe it."

He sold Monitor a new Raleigh twenty-eight-inch bicycle for a giveaway of little more than half the advertised price. The satisfied customer had barely left the shop when John got into his car and set off in search of Tomboy Farrell.

*

"It's only by the grace of God I heard about it in time," John Sheerman enthused to Martyn Murray and Christopher Rogan, seated before a blazing fire in his commodious parlour after tea. "In a situation like this you have to move fast and pull up your bridges behind you. The whole country will be trying to get on the bandwagon. What I'm saying is that when this man comes into his fortune he can bring more business to the three of us than we're fit to handle, provided we play our cards right. If we look after him and put him on his feet he's not going to let us down when he gets his hands on the money."

Martyn Murray owned a large drapery in the town and Christopher Rogan owned a prospering public house and groceries establishment. Neither of them was overly enthusiastic about the proposition.

"Before I'd invest money in any venture," Martyn declared, "I'd want to be sure of the return. This proposition doesn't make sense to me – we don't know for certain whether or not Tomboy Farrell will inherit a fortune."

"Even if there is a fortune, when will he get it?" Christopher asked. "And whenever he gets it, what's to make him give us his custom, or even pay us back whatever we might spend on him?"

John Sheerman was able to convince them. For a start, they knew he was a hard businessman, not noted for throwing money around. On top of that, his story was unassailable.

"Look here," he said, tapping the table with a finger to emphasise the points. "I read the letter with my own two eyes, there's no doubt whatsoever that he's inheriting a fortune in the near future.

"If I had any doubts about it before, I have none now. He spent nearly an hour with the American ambassador in the Phoenix Park today while I waited for him outside in the car. And when we were moving away, out rushes the ambassador to tell him not to worry, that he would personally look after the form for him and post it. As far as I'm concerned nothing could be clearer. This is none of your penny-ha'penny affairs. I felt I was doing a good turn by giving you the chance to join me in the venture, but if you don't feel like it I'll go it on my own."

John had been very impressed by the incident in the Phoenix Park. After the interview, when he was starting the engine to move off, he spotted the official rushing out after Tomboy to assure him on some point. This concern influenced John greatly. In the very brief interval he noted the man's debonair disposition, the clean-shaven pale face and most unusual and intriguing feature: his sleek black hair was combed back and there was a white patch of hair over the left ear.

"To tell you the truth, I'm inclined to go along with you against my better judgement, mainly because I know you so well," Martyn declared. "I was going to buy a bit of property and I'll have to leave it over if I take that road. But there's another angle to this: at the end of the day, you're the one to benefit the most. You'll sell him cars and hackney him around the country, you'll sell him petrol and wirelesses and gramophones. What is he going to buy from me – drink and groceries? There's no way I'm going to put in the same money as you."

John Sheerman appreciated the force of the argument. In

particular, although he had to keep silent about this, whatever arrangement might be made with Tomboy Farrell would include an agreement that intoxicating drink was out of bounds. Too many plans he knew about had perished down that road.

Christopher, the same way as Martyn, felt that John would be the main beneficiary. In the end an agreement was hammered out: for every hundred pounds invested by John the other two would contribute fifty pounds each. An initial sum of two-hundred pounds would be made available to Tomboy Farrell within the following week and the transaction, terms and conditions would be the sole responsibility of John Sheerman. Before the meeting concluded a bottle of whiskey was opened and glasses were touched to Tomboy Farrell's good health and fortune.

*

"The position is," John Sheerman expounded, "that you are coming into a fortune very shortly and you're not ready for it. Let me tell you, sonny, that handling a fortune is serious business and nobody succeeds in serious business if they are not prepared for it."

He was in Tomboy Farrell's kitchen in late afternoon and only the two men were present.

"Look, sonny," he continued "you'll be mixing with well-off, educated people and they'll be calling on you here. To give yourself a chance you'll have to make yourself respectable, and make this place presentable as well. The people that matter are the ones you'll be dealing with and they're not going to lower themselves. So you'll have to jack yourself up," the garage proprietor explained in idiomatic parlance. "And the same applies to Aggy. There are no half-measures in this."

Tomboy listened with the rapt and mesmeric attention of the disciples at the Sermon on the Mount. He shuffled and shrugged his shoulders, nodding his head appreciatively or in puzzlement at various points emphasised.

"You'll have begrudgers as well as plenty to jump on the bandwagon. Keep your wits about you, sonny. What you want is a reliable friend to help you first of all prepare for the sudden blast of riches and after that to enjoy them. There's money and time involved in this, and only a fool would invest if there's no guarantee of repayment with interest at the end of the day.

"I'll throw my cards face up on the table for you, sonny. Don't think I'm being personal because certain things have to be said and there's no easy way of saying them. Look at the cut of you – bad clothes, worn-out boots and dirty as a tramp. On top of that, if you are to succeed, you must know how to behave in company, how to carry yourself, how to talk, how to eat. In other words, yourself and Aggy have to be trained to be gentry. People think there's nothing to it, but let me tell you there's a hell of a lot.

"Then there's this place to look after. You're going to end up buying a mansion somewhere, but for the present this shack will have to do. Look at the state of it! There are sheds around the parish that are more presentable. Not a proper table nor a chair to sit on. Old boxes for stools and jam jars for mugs. No place to shit or piss. Can you see what I'm getting at?"

"Of course I can understand what yer makin' out," Tomboy replied. "But I'm not sure how I could go about it. I'll have to wait until I come into the money."

"Oh, by Jesus no, you're too late then! At that stage you'll have enough on your plate organising a business. Take a tip from me, sonny, it's now or never!"

"But how on earth can it be managed then?"

"Very simply! I've had discussions with friends and we're prepared to finance you up to a point and on certain conditions."

Tomboy was palpably enthused.

"Oh, I'll agree to anything," he declared. "You know what yer talkin' about an' I'll do whatever ye want me to."

"Very well then, sonny," John responded with obvious satisfaction. "This is the plan I have in mind.

"We will put the finances your way, as I said up to a reasonable point, and make the necessary arrangements in the bank for you to draw as required. Regarding your manner and dress, your way of life and behaviour, you will have to receive lessons on a regular basis. So will Aggy, although she hasn't as much ground to make up as yourself. There are two Rogan brothers and a sister living less than two miles from here and I believe they would be prepared to straighten you out. Their brother, Christopher, is a friend of mine. As far as improving this shack is concerned it will be up to you to engage someone suitable to do it without wasting any time.

"It's most important that you understand and agree to the conditions though, because otherwise we shake hands and part. But I think you'll agree that the terms are simple and reasonable. Firstly, when you get the fortune you will repay our outlay plus ten per cent. Secondly, you will have to deal with me, and a couple of others I nominate, exclusively for the goods and services we deal in. Thirdly, in all of this, complete confidentiality will be observed, not a word to anyone – the slightest breach in this regard would undermine the whole operation. Fourthly, you yourself will not consume intoxicating drink at any time – we know that you are not a drinking man. Fifthly, I reserve the right to pull out of the deal at any time and recoup all expenses should that be necessary. These are fair and essential stipulations. Are you prepared to sign an undertaking to that effect?"

"John," Tomboy responded enthusiastically, "I believe everything you want me to do is only fair an' right, seein' what yer doin' for me. There's not another man in the world would go to such rounds and spend such money to help. On top of everything else, when I get the money I'll make it worth yer while as well."

They shook hands firmly and arranged that John would call the following morning at ten o'clock and take Tomboy to sign the deal with a solicitor.

*

John Sheerman drove to his solicitor's office straight from Tomboy's house. The solicitor was in attendance and saw him without any wait. John explained his business, including the general background, and set out the points to be included in the agreement.

"You must be having me on," the lawyer laughed heartily into John's face.

John was peeved. "I'm absolutely serious about this. All I want you to do is draw up the agreement and it'll be signed tomorrow morning."

The solicitor adopted a more serious manner.

"John," he declared, "if you're not joking you must be out of your mind. I can't believe what you're telling me. This man could be either a swindler or a nutter!"

"Well he's not a swindler," John replied. "He hasn't the ability for that. And while he may be a blockhead I'm not relying on his story. I saw the letter myself and, furthermore, I saw the American Ambassador running after him and playing up to him. You need have no worry, the thing is straight."

"It would take more than that to convince me," the solicitor declared. "Give yourself a bit of time here, John, there's no sound reason for rushing into such a precarious and extraordinary situation. Hold your horses for a while."

John was incensed and exasperated.

"Look here," he stated firmly, "you've always been my solicitor and I've always paid you promptly for your work. Are you prepared to draw up this agreement for me or are you not? If you're not prepared to do it, I'll go elsewhere."

The solicitor paused and thought deeply, stroking his puckered forehead all the while.

"Yes, John," he replied, "of course you have been a good client of mine. I trust you feel I always gave full satisfaction on my side. And I would be deeply worried if I were to lose your patronage."

"You would, surely," John responded. "And you'd be the first man out to Tomboy Farrell looking for his business!"

"That may very well be the case, but it's a completely different issue. I have a duty of care to you and it would be wrong of me to ignore that. Give yourself space to think, John, get some tangible evidence regarding this alleged fortune, come back to me in a week or a fortnight when you have given more thought to the matter."

"Well, feck you anyway," were John Sheerman's parting words as he left, banging the door behind him.

He went immediately to another solicitor, who was less solicitous about the success of the venture. On the following morning he collected Tomboy at his home as arranged and, in less than an hour, the agreement was signed and sealed as a binding contract between the parties.

*

Christopher Rogan's spinster sister, Lena, and his bachelor

brothers, Alfred and Malachy, farmed about fifty acres and lived in a quaint two-storey house situated along a quiet country road. They were comfortably well-off and employed one labourer who turned a hand to everything, from polishing boots to milking and ploughing.

The Rogans regarded themselves as elite and lived up, or attempted to live up, to that billing. They had a pew in the church and were high on the various offerings lists. Stuck-up and patronising, they nevertheless managed to keep their assertive propensity within acceptable limits, people being amused rather than outraged at their often puerile manoeuvres. At threshing time, as an example, when a large number of locals would gather to assist, it was customary to provide for all a meal, dinner or tea depending on the time of the day. Invariably, elsewhere groups would be taken into the house and seated at random, wherever they might choose to sit. In Rogans, however, the wheat was separated from the chaff in the house as in the yard. Workers were segregated at the door, the better-off directed to the parlour and the poorer breed to the kitchen. This singling out was done with flair, however. Alfred Rogan, who never in his life engaged in manual work, would steer a worker towards the kitchen with a whisper into his ear.

"You're working very hard and must be ravenous with hunger – you'll get a much better meal in there," or "you'll find it far more comfortable in there."

Most workers had a preference for the kitchen in any event because everything, as well as the food, in the parlour was dainty and the higher standard of etiquette expected made the occasion somewhat stressful for grubby, sweating men engaged in hard manual labour.

In fact, even in the kitchen the food was far from satisfying.

There were vague criticisms of the poor, insubstantial fare. Prick McGinnity expressed the old adage that an empty sack won't stand. Pontius Pilate had a more original viewpoint: he claimed that a poor meal is like a bad confession – you feel worse afterwards than before it. In any event, nobody ever felt really comfortable dining at Rogans'.

When Tomboy and Aggy attended Rogans' for their first lesson they were seated in the kitchen and interviewed by Lena, who was in charge of the coaching. The first grilling was in relation to the fortune. At all times the two brothers were present as well, listening attentively always, interjecting occasionally or giving examples of proper, as well as improper, procedures. It was fully understood by the Rogans that their task was a difficult one that would take considerable time. To their surprise, progress was faster than expected. Although Tomboy was dull as ditch water, he was amenable and co-operative. In some ways his brainlessness was a positive factor because he had no self-consciousness or hang-ups. The outcome was that, thanks to a new bicycle, new clothes and grooming, as well as softening of raw edges, he was effectively a new man in a couple of months. Aggy was no less enthusiastic, and before long they were both promoted to the parlour.

The lessons they received related to personal hygiene, deportment and dress. They learned how to sit properly at the table, how to hold a knife and fork, how to eat, how to use a serviette, how to indicate by positioning the knife and fork whether or not another helping was required. As time went on, they were successfully acquiring the essential hallmarks of breeding and refinement. Lena Rogan and her brothers were very satisfied with the rate of progress. Of course, it would take a long time for the finer points to manifest themselves spontaneously

– like rubbing the corners of the mouth with a little finger or patting the mouth with a serviette at the dining table. But a solid foundation was undoubtedly soon established.

During the course of the training it was resolved that only the proper Christian names, Thomas and Agnes, would be used henceforward in relating to the two principals. It was even contemplated that Thomas's surname would be amended to O'Farrell as – according to Lena Rogan – the illustrious clan had been called before the time of Cromwell. But legal advice was that this could cause difficulties, particularly in regard to the legacy, so the proposal was dropped.

*

It was a cold and dark night as Thomas Farrell wheeled his unlighted bicycle along the road. One of the most serious hazards for pedestrians on the road at night was the unlighted bicycle, particularly in wet or windy conditions. In order to reduce the danger of such an accident in the dark the seasoned unlighted cyclist usually whistled or sang to announce his approach. The big problem about this was that it left the cyclist easy prey for a waylaying policeman. On this occasion Thomas could hear a euphonious whistle coming closer and closer. When he judged that the cyclist was within hearing range he pulled further into the grass margin and shouted a warning

"Careful there, be careful now!"

The cyclist instantly jumped off and approached with caution until the two men were almost rubbing shoulders.

"You'd want cats' eyes to see tonight," Thomas spoke out. "How on earth did you manage to stay on the road without landing in the ditch?"

The other cyclist was Pontius Pilate.

"I nearly did, several times," he confessed, "but I went slow and every time I felt the grass I pulled out again! Who the hell have I, anyway?"

"Thomas Farrell from Velmarstown."

"Oh, begod, Thomas, is it yerself that's in it? I saw ye goin' to town earlier this evenin'. And didn't I spot a brand new carbide lamp on yer bicycle?"

"You did surely. But it's the first time I used it and it was grand when I lit it up. Then a couple of hundred yards back it started to splutter and went out. I was tryin' to get to the nearest house to see if they could do anything for me."

"Sure come on an' I'll bring you up to the house with me. I should be able to help ye."

Before long they reached the house without incident and Pontius took Thomas into the dingy room. Pilate's wife was nursing a baby in front of a poor smoking log fire. There was good light from a double-wick paraffin lamp hanging on the wall under a projecting tin shield.

While Pontius proceeded to rectify the carbide lamp his wife pressed Thomas to have a cup of tea. He gratefully declined, explaining that it was little more than an hour since he had a sumptuous meal with friends in town.

"By the way," Pontius declared as he set about his task, "we're honoured to have a millionaire in the house. Everybody knows the good news, there's no use denyin'. The very best o' luck to ye!"

"Well I'm not exactly a millionaire at the moment but I'm hopin' to be one soon."

"The very best o' luck to ye anyway. It couldn't happen to a decenter man."

At this stage the carbide lamp was lighting perfectly and

Thomas was impressed.

"It's simple enough when ye understand it," Pontius explained. "All you have to do until the carbide is dead is set it for the right amount of water. You'll get used to it yerself in a short while. What happened was ye must have cut off the water."

"Thank you very much indeed," Thomas retorted. "I won't offer you any money at the present time but I'll remember you when things go through. I'll tell ye what, though," he continued as an afterthought, "I'm lookin' for a handyman to do up the house for me. It's a fairly big job and I don't know if you're interested or any good at that kind of thing. I expect there's a few months work in it an' if ye come to me I'll give ye fifteen shillings a week."

"Begod, that's not bad. Not bad at all. I was to take up a job next Monday in Oromtown at fourteen bob a week. It might last a bit longer than yours but I'd prefer your kind of work."

"Well then take it in the name o' God," urged the wife. "Ye'd be far nearer home as well."

The child in the cradle started to cry while the carbide lamp purred and glowed. Pontius grabbed Thomas's hand and shook it firmly.

"It's a deal," he declared. "I'll be with ye at cockcrow on Monday mornin.'"

*

Events in the life of Tomboy Farrell moved so rapidly and convincingly that even astute observers had difficulty in keeping abreast of developments. Except for a few hardline begrudgers, nobody now referred to him as the Twit. Some called him Thomas Farrell, a few added the title Mister, as befitted a gentleman, but universally the appellation 'Millionaire' applied and was generally considered complimentary and appropriate.

A few trivial problems proved somewhat intractable. As well as having two left feet, Thomas had two left hands. He could not manage the carbide lamp, no matter how hard he tried. In addition, his mastery of the bicycle was of a kind that did not do justice to his exalted standing. It was decided that a number of problems could be solved by providing him with a pony and trap. An excellent and suitable animal was purchased as well as an impeccably presented gig with side candle lanterns. The highly polished harness had solid silver mountings. This contrivance was suited admirably for short journeys, particularly when Thomas and Agnes were travelling together. In the dark, the candle-lit lamps were simple to control. Such a method of conveyance was considered more dignified than the common bicycle, which consequently was used thereafter on very infrequent occasions.

It was only a little over three months since Pontius Pilate was engaged to renovate the house, and the improvements were remarkable. A new roof of thatch had been applied, doors and windows replaced or repaired, walls patched and whitewashed, all timberwork painted. New furniture had been installed, including a large mahogany wardrobe for an extensive collection of suits and clothing. An impressive gramophone, a gift from John Sheerman, was conspicuous on the parlour table. Outside, old sheds had been repaired or demolished and, at the end of a stone pathway, through newly laid out and planted gardens, a latrine modelled on the local school system was provided. Paths and flowerbeds to the front complemented a very impressive setting.

"I must congratulate you, Thomas," John Sheerman declared, "on your choice of worker, however you foraged him out. This Pontius Pilate has done a great job for you. What kind of money are you paying him?"

"Sixteen shillings a week he gets. He started off at fifteen but looked for a shilling more when it came to the thatching, so I gave it to him and he turned out to be so good I left it that way. I'll only want him for a few more weeks."

"And why would he want more to attend the thatcher?"

"Well, John, the way he put it was that attending a thatcher is the meanest job in the country. As he said himself, a helper at thatching has his nose all day in the thatcher's arse. Anyway, he's good value and he has agreed to come back to me when this business is finished and I move to a bigger place."

A short time afterwards, Thomas Farrell and Agnes McDunphy announced their engagement. The date for the marriage was set for two months later. Corny yarns and jokes spread as is usual in relation to the event and the circumstances. Even Pontius Pilate could not resist a wry reflection when Thomas mentioned the happy news.

"Shur if ye intend to have a hape o' childer, now's the time to be movin'!"

A system had evolved whereby John Sheerman provided motor transport for Thomas whenever necessary. Sometimes, this was even on a daily basis. Occasionally, John himself did the driving but more frequently the head mechanic was the chauffeur and he had a special blazer and peaked cap to wear on those occasions. Like John, he operated in a manner that befitted a millionaire's minder – wiped off specks of real and imaginary dust on his clothes, opened the car door for him and bowed respectfully before closing it. With the announcement of the wedding, chauffeuring Agnes also involved considerable additional time and particular attention.

John Sheerman came to the conclusion that as the legacy affair was moving to a finality an improvement in the arrangement should be devised. He suggested to the engaged couple that they would shortly require a luxury car and that now was the time to acquire it. In the short term, it would be used as a hackney solely for their use and become their property on payment of the cost when the money came through. They were both pleased with the idea but a problem arose as to the choice of vehicle. It was agreed to acquire an Armstrong-Siddeley as the most prestigious and appropriate, but this choice was rescinded when advisers discovered that Eddy, Prince of Wales (so termed by the Millionaire's coterie), had such a car and, therefore, it would not be as exclusive as the situation demanded. The next choice was a Terraplane, but there was a delivery problem with this model. In the end, a Ford V8 was the favoured selection. Two weeks later, Thomas and Agnes enjoyed their maiden voyage to Dublin in the blue limousine and expressed almost entire satisfaction with the purchase. The occasion for the visit was to attend the Eucharistic Congress Mass in the Phoenix Park, where they were reputed to be seated next to the ambassadorial ranks. The reservation about the car, vaguely implied, related to the seating: although the leather upholstery was of a superior standard, and visually impressive, it was considered somewhat inappropriate for tender, blue-blooded buttocks, particularly on long, tiring journeys. Within a matter of days, soft, comfortable and colourful cushions provided a tolerable resolution of the sensitive dilemma.

*

No sooner was the wedding announced than the presents started to pour in. People came from near and far with assorted gifts, one trying to outdo another with their choices. For some reason, shoes for Agnes were the most popular items, but furniture, linen, household furnishings, ornaments and clothing were also high on the list. Quality, as well as quantity, was amazing; there was nothing inferior or shoddy that might be regarded as inappropriate in the prospective mansion of the Millionaire.

Among the presents that could be regarded as unusual were three wireless sets, two gramophones, and no less than six figure-reducing corsets fitted variously with four and six suspenders. Pontius Pilate could not subdue his penchant for quips when he irked Agnes by referring to the high-quality corsets from the expensive Abdo and Twilfit ranges. "A lot o' people want to help ye pull yerself together," he remarked.

As usual in such cases, the presents were stored and displayed in the residence of the bride. A couple of weeks before the wedding, the house was crammed to the doors and there was no place for any more. Presents received from then on were packed ceiling high in the bridegroom's house, and even there space would have run out were it not for the ingenuity of Pontius Pilate.

The question of security for the valuable presents then arose, for the period until a mansion could be acquired, but more particularly and immediately while the two houses would be vacant during the two-week honeymoon period. Agnes again came to the rescue by consulting her source. As a result, a week before the wedding, all the presents were dispatched to an undisclosed destination in Dublin, where they would remain safe until Thomas and Agnes moved into an appropriate permanent residence. This arrangement brought relief to a number of people who were concerned about the safety of the precious collection.

In the week before the big day, the feverish excitement extended far beyond the boundaries of Geblik parish. People talked about nothing but the Millionaire's wedding. Stories of doom and boom spread, most of which could not be authenticated.

A wicked rumour was put about by some begrudger that the legacy was a fantasy thought up by Thomas Farrell and that the wedding arrangements were about to be cancelled. Monitor Crawley, the first herald to publicise the legacy, had followed developments with a particular personal interest, as well as a sense of responsibility and reputation, and he was troubled with the news. He decided to check the information at source and, with considerable difficulty, succeeded in confronting Agnes. She was aware of the important part he had inadvertently played in dissemination of the good news, and while nobody could ever claim she had any accountability in that regard it was nonetheless obvious to some extent that Monitor's credibility was at stake and it was in her own interest to be frank and forthcoming with him.

"Tell me," he demanded bluntly, "is this thing of Thomas's straight?"

"Thomas's thing is as straight as a rush," she assured him. And, as he put it aphoristically afterwards, who was to know more about the ins and outs of the thing than Agnes?

According to another story, Agnes, in preparation for the wedding, underwent a procedure whereby – it was claimed – she had her face lifted. The process was so successful that Thomas, waiting for her in the Gresham Hotel, failed to recognise her when she passed him by in the foyer. Some people felt the account was exaggerated, others believed that even altering the slant of her hat could be too big a test for his faculty of recognition.

A certain amount of sourness and resentment was inevitable when individuals who had an exalted notion of their importance failed to make the list of invitations. It was accepted as unthinkable that there would be any place for commoners or plebs – only individuals of means and importance were considered eligible to be guests. This was not a cause of any contention or friction because the Millionaire had cultivated a very favourable relationship with the community. He did this mainly by responding positively to requests for favours when the legacy would be realised. Not all of the appeals were specific or direct, in fact most of them were in the biblical format of *Lord, remember me when you come into your Kingdom.* Often, too, people would refer to negative circumstances in their lives and get a promise of redress. When the Millionaire visited the parochial house the priest apologised for the poor decorative condition of the place due to scarce resources. There was an immediate pledge to help.

"Don't worry about it, Father," he assured him. "I can see you're a bit stuck for space here as well, ye could do with another storey. This time next year ye won't know the place."

The housekeeper, who overheard the conversation, would recall the veracity of the prediction one year later.

The selection of the guests was the responsibility of Lena Rogan and it was a tribute to her diligence and expertise that eighty people of sufficient means and eminence to merit an invitation were identified and seventy of those responded positively. This did not include ten clergymen, four of whom were parish priests, and a select group of twelve for whom Agnes was responsible. True, two of the biggest landowners in the parish were unable, for what were considered flimsy reasons, to attend, but they sent presents. Otherwise, the occasion was an organisational triumph. Christy the Kithen, who was an acknowledged expert on matters of historical consequence, claimed that, with regard to the function and the impressive list of distinguished guests, no event of comparable importance had been experienced since the year 1170 when Strongbow married Eva in the august precincts of Waterford Cathedral.

*

The parish church in Lectastown was crowded for the wedding with the overflow congregation extending out to the yard gates. A long line of private and hired cars such as was never seen before, decorated with flags and ribbons, parked along the public road. The day was fine and there was a carnival atmosphere typical of rare momentous social occasions.

Dressed in a smart-cut turquoise-coloured two-piece suit, with veiled hat and silver shoes, the bride looked elegant and relaxed. People abstrusely expressed the view that she didn't show half her age. The bridegroom was dressed in a navy blue double-breasted suit, white shirt with gold monogrammed cufflinks and red tie with gold tie-pin decorated in Celtic interlacing style. Miss Laetitia Cooper-Jones, the bridesmaid, was attired in an ensemble that matched the bride, while the best man, Aloysius Farrell, a distant cousin of the groom, sported an outfit similar to the groom but with less imposing finery. Red carnations were provided for all lapels.

The ceremony with nuptial mass took little more than an hour, which must be a record, or close to one, for such a high-society wedding. Afterwards, the principals had extreme difficulty in getting through the crowd of well-wishers who threw oaten meal at the happy couple, shook hands, clapped and cheered. Eventually, an escape was organised and the noisy impressive motorcade set off on the twenty-mile journey to Drogheda.

The reception was held in the White Horse Hotel and was of the standard reserved for royalty. At the same time, all chauffeurs, drivers and attendants were entertained in a separate part of the premises, an unusual arrangement which proved satisfying and successful – it was said that the fare and craic in the secondary location exceeded any routine reception outing.

Pre-eminent occasions of this nature seldom take place without a hitch, and it was unfortunate that on the day before the wedding Martyn Murray and Christopher Rogan succumbed to sudden serious indispositions and had to receive immediate medical attention. They were both confined to bed and their absence, together with their wives, led to an urgent reorganisation of the head table as they were at the top of the invited list. This slight hiccup was, however, handled adroitly and, while the absence of the eminent guests caused some fuss initially, such relatively insignificant matters were forgotten as the wining and dining took over.

When the sumptuous meal was finished the speeches started. All ten priests spoke in glowing terms of the married couple. There were special references to the qualities that distinguished Thomas Farrell: his individuality, astuteness and foresight, but above all his generosity. Anecdotes were recounted and incidents recalled that portrayed a hidden philanthropic – even noble – nature. All the contributions received clamorous ovations.

Then the music, dancing, drinking and profound discussions got into full swing and time flew by. There was disbelief when the hour for departure arrived. It took several efforts before Thomas and Agnes Farrell were safely seated in the Millionaire's car to begin the journey to Dublin where the Clarence Hotel was booked for the two-week honeymoon.

*

There was great excitement at the Cross of the Line where an enormous crowd waited to welcome home the Millionaire and his wife from the honeymoon, chauffeured in the Ford V8 car. It was a delightful July evening, a fortnight after the wedding, and the married couple were expected at eight o'clock. Unbeknownst to them, the arrangement was to congregate at this point, about a mile from their home with the Millionaire's trap, into which the couple would be transferred from the car, and pulled manually to musical accompaniment for the final mile. At ten minutes to eight a light was set to a huge pile of tinder, and within a short space of time the flames and smoke of a massive bonfire could be seen far and wide. Soon it was nine o'clock, the fire had burned low and there was no sign of the arrival. Still the carnival mood continued with music, singing and dancing, all eyes focused towards the Dublin direction. By half past nine an uneasy quietness had affected the scattered crowd. Patience was running out fast until the sound of a car coming from the Skell direction was heard. As it rounded the corner a great cheer went up when everyone recognised the Millionaire's Ford V8. Just as suddenly the cheering died down as the car came closer and it was noted there was nobody in it but the driver, John Sheerman's head mechanic and designated chauffeur for the Millionaire. He was not attired in the silver-buttoned livery and peaked cap that he normally wore when on escort duty. The car came to a halt and as the crowd pressed around the driver jumped out.

"They're not comin' home at all," he shouted to the gaping throng. "It's all over. There's no fortune, it was all a cod!"

Some people coughed, scratched their heads and looked at one another. Others challenged the announcement angrily. There were remonstrations that some mistake had been made.

"Don't be foolin' yourselves! John Sheerman is in a bad way over it. He burned the uniform today. I couldn't get out any sooner to warn ye. It's gospel, that I may die, there's no fortune, it was all a cod!"

If the heavens had opened the effect could not have been more traumatic. A murmur reverberated through the stricken throng – *There's no fortune, it was all a cod!* There followed a fragmentation into small irregular confused groupings. Most were shattered and speechless, particularly those who had invested beyond their means to provide wedding presents or had sought to endear themselves to the Millionaire in various imaginative ways. But there were others who claimed that they were never taken in by the hoax.

"I never believed the fucker from the start," Prick McGinnity claimed. "Shur isn't he the greatest bollox in the parish."

"Not while you're around," someone who had been duped chimed in.

Strong and loud words were exchanged, there were bickerings and accusations. A few scuffles petered out without serious incident. It was unbelievable that there was no crock of gold at the rainbow's end. People started to drift away until finally, as darkness began to fall, only Prick McGinnity and two of his companions remained.

"We better throw this in off the road before we go," Prick suggested, referring to the now redundant trap.

They unceremoniously bundled the polished and decorated buggy against the bushes in the wide grass margin. And before leaving Prick relieved himself against it with the casualness of a dog against a lamp post.

*

Ten days after the wedding John Sheerman met with Martyn Murray and Christopher Rogan in his parlour. The mood was cold, relations strained and communications tense. John was pale and distraught. There had been other dire contacts and acrimonious encounters between the three men over the previous week.

"Christopher and I just had to try and sort out the stupid mess we got ourselves into," Martyn explained. "It was madness from the start, I can't believe that I allowed myself to be talked into it! There's no legacy and there never was. Our money is gone, not a hope of getting a penny back, and only we acted we'd still be pouring it down the drain."

He then went through the steps that were taken to establish the position. Christopher Rogan in his public house had been given information about a dapper stranger who was seen a few times calling on Aggy McDunphy, for longish spells, around two hours at a time. The purpose of the man's visits was the subject of some speculation, but was considered seriously improper. Rather than discuss the matter with John Sheerman, who was firm and stubborn in his views, Christopher and Martyn engaged an investigator to examine the whole situation and they received a report two days before the wedding. It was so disconcerting that both men had to receive medical help over several days for shock and nervous debility.

Although the report did not specifically identify the actual perpetrator of the hoax, as Martyn rhetorically asked, what did it matter anyway? Whenever in the past John Sheerman had been questioned regarding the authenticity of the legacy claim he responded with a stock reply that was impossible to challenge: the letters from the law attorney are there to prove it. But it transpired that the lawyer in question had been removed from the rolls some five years previously for serious breaches of the professional code. It was also established that there was no record of any communications with the American ambassador in relation to the matter and that, in any event, he would only have a perfunctory role in any such circumstances.

Enquiries revealed that there was no official by the name of Pedro McPartlin employed permanently at the American Embassy. A gentleman of that name was, however, engaged until recently on a casual basis in relation to general filing arrangements. He attended on the last Friday of every month.

It was difficult to get much information about Pedro McPartlin except that he was the only son of a wealthy family that lived on the South Circular Road, Dublin. He was remembered by neighbours as a very bright but rebellious boy who, after graduation in college, earned some notoriety as a playboy and got into serious difficulties for which a long-serving skivvy by the name of McDunphy took the rap. She was sacked at the time but it was rumoured that she received a generous reward for her exceptional loyalty. A relationship of sorts with the family was also maintained because Miss McDunphy was seen occasionally afterwards paying brief visits to the house.

"The reality is," Christopher Rogan declared angrily to John Sheerman, "that you were conned by trickery and we were taken in by you."

John Sheerman was speechless. He sat on his chair with an elbow on the table and blew erratically through a nervous cupped hand that patted his pursed mouth. The normally ruddy face was as white as his well-laundered shirt.

"The question we have to decide," Martyn Murray asked, "is what are we going to do about it? What can we do to get something back?"

"This man owns a cottage on five acres of land," Christopher Rogan pointed out. "His wife also owns a house. According to accounts they got wedding presents that would stock Cleary's

Store in O'Connell St. But again we have the trickery – nobody knows where these are now. In broad daylight they were deliberately moved out of reach while the gulled looked on – in fact collaborated in the connivance. I believe we should go to a solicitor and take the case to court."

This suggestion brought an instant reaction from John Sheerman. He jumped out of his chair and paced the room holding the back of his head with one hand and waving the other.

"Oh, Jesus Christ, no!" he pleaded. "Aren't we bad enough as it is without having it plastered in *The Meath Chronicle* for the whole country to read! We'd be the laughing stock of the place if people knew we were taken in by the two greatest mugs on this earth."

"That is a major consideration," Martyn agreed. "But the problem is more involved than that. You see, the Millionaire claims he did nothing wrong and that there's a conspiracy against him. Nobby Lanigan interviewed him in the Clarence Hotel. It seems he grew up with the delusion that he was going to inherit a fortune. This was in some way bolstered in his final days at school by a reference the teacher is supposed to have made. When the Twit told the story to McDunphy she sought advice from this rogue, Pedro McPartlin. It was there the collusion began, so who is to blame? And where the hell would you start or finish in the courts? Where would the costs come from?"

More harsh words followed, accusations and recriminations. John Sheerman sought some solace in his devastation by expressing contempt and reprobation for Thomas Farrell and Agnes McDunphy.

"They're the two greatest halfwits of all time," he declared.

"You're wrong there, John," Martyn responded with a grave shake of the head. "There are at least three greater fools!"

"Yes," Christopher agreed. "And we know which of the three is the bum champion."

*

It was a big fair day in Skell and the streets were covered with people and cattle. Business premises were perked up for the occasion. In the public houses the floors were covered with oaten straw or sawdust and the snugs were given a few strokes of a damp cloth. Yards were swept and temporary signs erected. Hucksters, entertainers and charlatans took up positions at street corners and other vantage points. The excitement, jostling, music, sounds and smells were features of a successful country market occasion.

John Sheerman was in his spacious shop which fronted a large garage and yard when Monitor Crawley called to purchase a chain for his bicycle. Trade was brisk. Although it was over twelve months since the wedding of the Millionaire, John was still very sensitive about his blunder; the ridicule, as well as the financial loss, induced a rawness that would take a very long time to heal. He attributed a considerable amount of blame to Monitor, who had first given him the startling news of the alleged legacy. Consequently, he was unable to serve him civilly at the counter.

"Will somebody look after this man," he called out disdainfully as he moved to attend another customer.

Some time later in the afternoon John Sheerman was in his office in the corner of the showroom when he noticed a debonair visitor enter. The whiskered gentleman wore a wide-brimmed black hat and a long, loose black cloak. He carried a ferruled walking cane with poise and had rings on fingers of both hands. His demeanour was polished and dramatic.

"Who the hell is this joker?" John muttered as he moved forward to attend him, diverting a diligent assistant seeking to serve. On a big fair day in Skell, all kinds of characters appeared but the stranger was exceptional by any standard. John's instinct told him the man was a distinguished actor and he had a vague notion that he had seen him before with those penetrating eyes in some play or other: *East Lynne* came to mind, probably because he had seen it several times on account of its local appeal, as the author was reputed to be related to a successful business family in the town of Skell.

"How can I help you, sonny?" he inquired in his usual business manner.

"I'll tell you what it is, sir," the stranger began. "I'm arranging a tour and – would you believe? – looking for a means of transport. The car I'm looking to buy must be big, reliable and cheap. I believe you have a Ford V8 that fits the bill."

"By God, that's a tall order," John replied tactfully. "But you weren't misled, sonny, I have the rale McCoy for you. Come out till you see it yourself and I'll take you for a drive."

"Before that, sir, in all fairness, I'd want to know the price. There's no use wasting time if it's out of my reach."

"The price is right, a bargain you can't afford to miss! One-hundred-and-fifty pounds with a full tank of petrol."

The stranger was taken aback.

"Oh, dear!" he exclaimed. "I must have got the story wrong. Crossed lines somewhere. That's over twice as much as I was given to understand."

John was visibly annoyed as well as disappointed.

"Well, sonny, is it a bargain or a present you're after? This is a car that's as good as the day it left the factory. It couldn't be sold at a penny less. I'm not here to be insulted, you know."

"Oh, begging your pardon, don't misunderstand me, sir," the stranger abjectly pleaded. "The information I got was that the car had a history, you were anxious to get rid of it but finding a difficulty in getting a buyer."

"There's a history about it all right," John agreed. "It was bought for an actor like yourself but the play went bust and there was no cash in the kitty."

"Not an unusual occurrence, I can assure you," commented the stranger. "By the way," he added inquisitively, "what kind of actor was he?"

"A comedian," John responded.

"Oh", said the stranger, "the hardest role of all."

"No, not for this man," John expounded. "It came to him naturally. He was a born clown, but lost the plot!"

"Well, unfortunately," observed the stranger, "in acting, perfection doesn't always pay the bills. Extravagance is inevitable in order to make the unskillful laugh while it makes the judicious – like your good self, sir – grieve. But money makes the mare go. And I'm afraid my problem is I don't have the money to buy your car, however much I may wish to have the vehicle fit for a king. My total and wholehearted apology, sir. But since I am here, maybe you could help me on another, though smaller, score. I note your extraordinary selection of gramophone records."

"The biggest range in the country," John claimed proudly, disappointed with the dashed expectations about the sale of the car but heartened that some business might be transacted.

"For over a year I'm looking for a particular gramophone record," the stranger explained, "but without success. Unfortunately, I don't know the name of the song, though I'd recognise it on the spot if I heard the first few bars. The singer is bewitching and, as far as I can recall, relatively unknown. There's a chorus, a duet with a beguiling female charmer."

"Well that's the strangest enquiry I ever got," John replied, "and on a busy fair day. Could you come back at another time and I'll play some records for you to see if we can help?"

"No, unfortunately," the customer replied. "I have never been in this town before and don't have any plans to come here again. But I'll understand, sir, if you can't oblige in the circumstances."

John was in a quandary. The stranger was so impressive and fascinating that he was reluctant to let him go without trying his best to be helpful, however hopeless the quest seemed.

"Can you give me any better lead on it?" he asked. "Sure I could spend hours going through the piles and not find what you want."

"I appreciate that and I'll be thankful for your help. The singer is, as I said, enchanting and the song was all the rage for a while. It is elegiac in nature."

"Elegiac?"

"Yes, you know what I mean – plaintive."

John became more curious and picked out a number of records. The first one he played was *The Donkey's Serenade*. After a few lines the stranger shook his head. For the next quarter of an hour John put on one record after another until it was obvious they were making no headway. Finally, he had enough.

"It's pointless," he said. "If you find out the name of the record come back to me and I'll try to help you."

The stranger thanked him profusely, tightened his cloak and moved towards the door. As he was about to put his hand on the knob he suddenly turned around and tapped his forehead lightly.

"I have it, I have it," he cried. "The name of the song has just come back to me!"

"Good man, yourself," John exclaimed. "What is it called, sonny?"

"It's called *The Millionaire Fantasy!*"

John Sheerman froze for a moment, then with the blood gushing to his head he impulsively picked up a bicycle pedal crank that was lying on the counter and flung it recklessly after the sneering pretender who had, at that stage, passed through the panelled lobby door. As the glass panel in the door shattered behind him he was already out on the footpath and passing the shop window. At the centre of the window he paused and taking off his hat bowed unctuously towards John Sheerman. What mesmerised John was not the histrionic antics but the man's sleekly black hair combed back; there was an incongruous white patch over the left ear.

The bizarre experience unnerved John Sheerman. With the commotion that arose he was delayed in getting out onto the street and when he arrived there the stranger was gone. It mattered little. What could be done anyway? He went straight across the street to a busy pub and ordered a double whiskey. The place was noisy, packed mostly with farmers, gombeens, blockers and tanglers, all preoccupied with their own agendas. Someone asked him concernedly how business was.

"Fair to middling," he replied.

"Go on outta that wit' ye, Mr Sheerman," another remonstrated. "Shur you always do well! An' why wouldn't ye, sellin' everything from a needle to an anchor!"

"It's a peculiar thing," John mused audibly, "that no matter what you stock there's always someone calling that you don't have the right article for. I had two such callers today."

"And what was it ye hadn't got for them?"

"A loaded double-barrelled shotgun," he replied, offhandedly.

*

Within a year of the legendary wedding Fr Drake suffered a stroke, from which he died. The housekeeper, for some reason, recalled the Millionaire's prophetic words: "This time next year, ye won't know the place." The Millionaire's own house had become dilapidated, with weeds and briars over most of the grounds. Thomas Farrell never returned to Geblik but obtained permanent employment with a titled estate owner as a caretaker in north county Dublin. According to reports, he filled the position with distinction.

A few people who became acquainted with the Millionaire in later years noted his aversion for the people of Geblik, whom he associated with an ignominious plot to deprive him of his inheritance. If Agnes brooded on the perils of plotting she kept such thoughts to herself. Events often pass without recognition of obscure pivotal ramifications, even by those centrally involved; credits and debits are sometimes placed in the wrong columns.

And so the people of the parish marvelled into future generations at the genius and coolness of an inconsequential twit who with impunity masterminded an audacious plot that fooled the world, ensuring immortality in the annals of Geblik lore.

Poaching, Appropriation and Deceitfulness
As A Normal Way Of Life

Nancy Pilate gave birth to a son in the maternity section of the County Home, Trim, on April 1, 1929. People in the parish of Geblik, or the few of them who had any interest in the event, were at first suspicious that the report was initiated by a prankster. Even Prick McGinnity was cagey when he heard the news.

"April fool!" he responded. "It's an April fool. Janey mack, if it's true isn't God the quare joker!"

Although he was subjected to disparagement and innuendo by a few righteous and outraged craw-thumpers, Pontius Pilate took developments more or less in his stride. There was no indication that censorious remarks, pitched at the right tone to reach his ear, caused him any significant unease. On the other hand, he responded with exhilaration to complimentary observations. And there was a share of these, although some might be barbed, or have a sting in the tail, like those made by Black Michael.

"Begod, Pontius, ye're a great wan. A son in two months, wha? If ye're able to keep it up ye'll have a football team in no time at all! Aye, if ye're able to keep it up, wha! Ye're a powerful man to ride a bicycle – I mane the two-legged wans, ha, ha!"

Christy the Kithen's view typified a common conception. "Weeds spread like hell," he claimed, "no matter what happens."

The son was christened James but would more pretentiously be called Séamus on account of the resurgence of Irish pride and nationalism. Within twelve months another son was born, this time at home with a midwife in attendance. He was named Peter and called Peadar.

Times had been getting harder for Pontius. Work was sporadic, at least work for which there was pay or tangible recompense. Competition for engagement with penurious farmers was intense and partial payment was often in kind – food, milk or fuel. There were spells with the county council on roads, in quarries and gravel pits. Latterly, there was work with the Irish Land Commission, building ditches, erecting houses and laying or improving roads or laneways.

For extensive in-between periods there was unemployment and the dole. Free milk was provided and could be collected at nominated centres, a pint per child per day, for impoverished families that qualified. There was also Dev's free meat, regarded by his political opponents as an inventive handout to bribe or cajole the impoverished masses as much as a food supplement. It worked both ways, erratically. Due to the heightening dissension of the Economic War, Britain banned the importation of Irish cattle, and distribution of the enormous meat surplus among a starving population was essentially a pragmatic alternative to dumping. That was the first time Séamus Pilate saw or tasted meat, other than the occasional domestic fowl or rabbit. What really intrigued him was the pencil stuck in the joint. He longed for a pencil to scribble on paper, a contrivance that he had seen with other children and which appealed to his imaginative impulse, but was dismayed to discover that a skewer does not have a graphite core.

Pontius was an indifferent husband and father. He never fitted comfortably into that role, though undoubtedly he tried in a desultory kind of way. But he lacked a sense of responsibility, of commitment; at heart, he remained a free and easy bachelor lad. For nearly four years the family lived in a two-roomed thatched cabin rented for a shilling a week. It was dark, damp and rat infested. Then they moved to a new county council cottage on one acre of ground, and this miraculous bounty was supplemented by an equally stupendous Irish Land Commission accommodation holding of five acres. His activities during the Troubles advanced his entitlements to these benefits. He was not as fortunate as those who received freebies of new houses and twenty-five-acre farms from the Land Commission, but then he was incomparably luckier than the many deserving applicants who got nothing.

Pontius could not be faulted for his efforts and intentions regarding management of the new acquisitions. He planted a huge garden and laurel hedges only to see them destroyed, and relationships undermined, by ravaging goats. A goat's milk is nutritional, and goats thrive on herbs and in conditions where a cow would not survive. In bad times, goats' milk played a big part in keeping hunger and disease, if not death, from many an unfortunate man's door. The goat was the poor man's cow. But the goat is an extremely nimble animal, almost impossible to fence in, and delights in the predacious destruction of vegetation in gardens with impunity. Consequently, where there were goats it was inevitable that there would be trespass and destruction, with constant serious rows and continuous bad feelings. On occasions, the repercussions were so grave that disputes were resolved in the courts and life-long animosities and estrangements resulted. If there was one single factor that, above all others, could cause the most peaceful community to erupt into factions of malevolence and hostility, it was the duplicitous goat, the poor man's greatest friend and worst enemy. And Pontius Pilate kept two goats, as did all the impoverished families in the area.

Undoubtedly the greatest cause for dissension and unrest in a rural community was poverty. Unemployed labourers had little or no income and yet they and their families had to subsist. A modicum of food and fuel was essential for survival and, consequently, in bad times farmers' lands were continuously under threat. Bushes and branches of trees were cut and removed, fencing posts were loosened and taken away, and damage was caused by encroachment on lands to poach as well as to pillage. Farmers could only police a limited number of locations at the one time and so they were bound to lose out where extended areas were under threat. In spite of improving political and social conditions, the miserable labourer was in many ways as repugnant in the new emerging Ireland as at the height of the despotic landlord. A certain apportionment of drudgers was, of course, not only tolerable but essential in terms of expediency and commerciality. But in Geblik, as elsewhere, the number of families living at destitution level was a constant and irreconcilable social strain.

On top of the general conditions that shaped the destiny of Pontius Pilate he had personality traits that compounded the adverse circumstances. While he was exceptionally clever and talented, and generally thought out matters carefully, he could blindly ignore a conclusion or omit a crucial link. Also by nature he was impetuous and impatient, a decided disadvantage in difficult and pressing situations. And he enjoyed a drink. Or two. He had his good points, though. No matter how he was wronged or offended he never harboured a grudge and he had a truly profligate disposition to be helpful. But in his own affairs he was inconsistent, often leaving tasks undone; he would be committed and enthusiastic up to a point and then bizarrely lose interest. At times, he might attempt to repair a clock or watch. It would be taken asunder and reassembled several times with extraordinary skill and patience. Then suddenly an assortment of cogged wheels and springs and screws would be gathered up into a cup or bowl and placed on a high shelf crowded with the results of similar endeavours. Or he might content himself reading a borrowed book – at such times, if the roof caved in, or the house went on fire, he would scarcely take notice.

Regularly, at night-time, in front of a blazing fire, with no one else in the house but his wife and two children, he would clear his throat, close his eyes and, leaning back in the chair, sing a medley of Irish songs with the passion of a professional entertaining a discerning audience. In a pub he could bring instant silence to a boisterous rabble with incomparable renditions. Often in those circumstances conditions at home might be appalling – little food, no fire and a frigid relationship with his wife. But he had that incredible gift – or fatal flaw – whereby he could divorce himself from reality and live for the moment. His wife, Nancy, suffered heroically and incessantly to keep devastation at bay, continuously barely scraping through. The suffering was not always in silence but Pontius could invariably take off and bang the door behind him when the rows became intense; it was his way of refusing to face reality or concede an argument, of rejecting common sense and logic. To the outside world, the family appeared to be normal, just about holding its own in the desperate struggle for survival. Maybe that was true – if the circumstances of all other households in the parish were explored many of them, if not all, even in the slipstream of a resurgent nation, might have been only marginally higher than the brute animal level.

Pontius was honest and truthful in a restricted and pragmatic way that might not always meet the stipulations of the tuppenny catechism. How, for example, could someone who regularly had to steal branches of trees on neighbouring farms for fuel, reconcile such behaviour with the obligations of the Seventh Commandment? Well, there's always a way, isn't there? How can someone who has to live on his wits for survival relate to the biblical paradigm of the man in whom there is no guile? Then, we're all actors, aren't we? And if the line must be breached at one pressure point, where is the logic of being overly concerned about other blurs or blotches? But in the sense of being reliable and giving good value to employers he had no peer.

Overall, it was the man's marital role and incompetence in financial affairs that created the greatest problems, that exposed his greatest flaws. There was no love or feeling in the marriage, just a social obligation, perversely imposed and unenthusiastically – even regretfully – undertaken. Marriage was basically a licence for carnal indulgence and, driven by a raw animal instinct, he took advantage of his conjugal rights as a sole sacrificial recompense, a purpose in life.

The difficulty about money was an ever-present problem, particularly during spells of unemployment. Finance had to be found in some way or other that might not be strictly orthodox but still was not publicly odious and did not involve prosecution or appearing in a court of law. One of the ways Pontius found of supplementing a derisory income was by poaching. He caught rabbits and hares, and, since the days of despotic landlordism were over, farmers were generally pleased to allow those destructive creatures to be trapped and snared on their lands. But an equally remunerative activity, more daring and exciting, was the poaching of fish in streams and rivers. This was an area where Pontius Pilate excelled.

*

Pontius Pilate's poaching activities on the rivers were divided mainly into two periods of the year, summer and winter. In summer he bagged loads of trout and in winter salmon returning from the sea to spawn were the target. Eels could be caught at almost any time.

He fished occasionally in the normal way with rod and line but caught comparatively few fish in this manner. However, this exercise was generally only intended to evaluate the situation in the waterways and to decide when was the best time to shift the fish. There were several ways of doing so but bagging was the simplest and most popular method of poaching trout in the streams and small rivers during the summer months.

Bagging trout was extremely simple. The bag was made by cutting out the bottom of a sack and sowing into it a circular piece of light wire mesh with around one-inch-square apertures. A bullwire frame was sown to the mouth of the sack, to keep it open, and to this a short handle was fitted. The operator then simply walked in the stream facing the flow, held the bag first to one bank, then the other, prodding with a stick up to a couple of yards beyond the bag under the bank where the fish sought cover. Most of the trout in the tight and muddy conditions darted directly and blindly into the bag. Pontius would lift up the bag and look into it every few yards. Generally silvery trout would be leaping around on the wire mesh. If they were not on the big size, or if there were only two or three of them, he might continue the exercise and only remove the fish into a sack attached to his shoulder when he had a considerable catch. Invariably, he had an assistant walking with him along the bank watching out in case the water bailiff or, much less likely, a Garda should appear on the scene. At the end of the operation the sack of fish would be emptied on the ground and divided as fairly as possible by

Pontius. He would then allow his assistant to select which one of the two piles he preferred. Unfairness or cheating was out of the question, an anathema to an honest poacher. There was nearly always a good return from bagging.

Another method, though less favoured by Pontius, was by blowing up the river. This could be carried out successfully only at deep holes. A stick of gelignite would be penetrated with a pencil and a detonator and a small length of fuse pushed into the cavity. Usually, a piece of cloth was tied around the unit to prevent it from falling apart. On occasion, Pontius would rip out an inside pocket from his coat and use it for this purpose. Then it was a matter of lighting the fuse, throwing it into the deepest part of the hole and rushing to cover for safety until the thud of the explosion a few seconds later. Both banks of the river would tremble with the blast and all dead and injured fish float to the top of the water and could be collected in a shallow stretch on the downstream side. This mode was well known to poachers but infrequently used because the necessary components were not easily available.

Without any doubt, the most effective way of divesting a river of virtually all its sizable aquatic vertebrates was to draw a large net along its length by means of ropes pulled and manipulated by men on both banks. This system, if properly organised, left almost no escape for fish, but therein was the problem: proper organisation required a large number of skillful and schooled operators to control and draw the net, and then invariably transport the catch along extended stretches of river. In addition, such nets were very bulky, there was considerable time involved and always the danger of the water bailiff arriving on the scene. To poach safely in this fashion it would be necessary to have the bailiff effectively constrained for several hours, a task which even the most hardened poacher would hardly countenance. Because of all these considerations, and the significant cost involved, this sophisticated method of poaching was rare. In fact, there was only one such operator in all of the region, Colonel Richard Harrington, a retired British army officer who lived in an adjoining parish. His training equipped him to be an expert without equal at this specialised method of avant-garde appropriation. Equally important, he had the commercial contacts to be able to dispose promptly of a large haul of fish for worthwhile gain. Inconceivably, because of his lifestyle of travel and living away from home, his name never came to the attention of the authorities.

Catching salmon during the spawning season could be done in any of those ways but gaffing was the most popular means. A gaff is a steel hook attached to a handle and this could be legally used by licensed fishermen to land a large fish caught on a line. But the gaff used by poachers had long poles for handles, many of them capable of stretching to the centre of the river. The hook was about the thickness of a pencil with a diameter of about three inches. It had to be barbed, although amateur poachers sometime improvised with a simple converted bacon hook, but many a salmon escaped on that account although properly struck. The brake spindle of a bicycle was considered the ideal rod from which to make a gaff hook but, because of its temper, it was very difficult to forge into shape.

Pontius Pilate had his own gaff which he had made himself. In the spring of the year he cut three or four long, sinewy stems in a neighbouring plantation and these were put away for seasoning all through the summer. When the poaching season arrived, he selected the best pole and attached the steel gaff to it with white cord. The white cord was important as a guide over the stationary salmon, particularly in the lamplight. Aim was always for the head in order to hook the fish around centre back. Sometimes, especially if the cord got dirty or discoloured, he tied a piece of white paper at this point as well. A carbide lamp was preferable to a flashlamp to identify the fish in the river but the battery lamp was far handier. The night had to be dark for a successful operation and normally three took part: a gaffer, someone to hold the lamp and a lookout. In the previous days the river would have been reconnoitred to determine the exact locations of the spawning beds. Occasionally, salmon were gaffed during daytime but this required greater expertise.

The gaff was a very cherished and personal possession of the poacher. On one occasion, Pilate came across a salmon which had escaped an encounter and it had a gaff with a short broken handle attached stuck in its back. He captured the salmon and, later in the week, affixed a new pole to the gaff hook. On the following Sunday he took it to another river and was in the act of using it when a fellow poacher, Sandy Rogan, appeared on the opposite bank.

"That's my gaff," he shouted across the moment he saw it.

"It's not," Pontius replied firmly. "How could it be yours?"

"It's my gaff surely," Sandy insisted. "I bought the steel rod in Mooney's garage for fourteen pence an' I paid a shillin' to Jemmy the Blacksmith to make it."

"Well, if it's yours tell me where I found it an' I'll give it to ye."

"Ye got it on the Mill River at the Black Hole an' it was stuck in a salmon."

"I did not," Pilate insisted, "but there it's for ye anyway if ye're so mad about it." He confessed to an associate afterwards that he got it within a hundred yards of the Black Hole and it was stuck in a huge salmon that was as hard to handle as a bull calf.

Poaching was always a perilous business. It was a distraction for daring men with stout hearts. In the previous season the bailiff had tracked down a poaching gang on a Saturday night near Hal's Hole, on the point of gaffing a salmon. He was within about twenty yards of them when he shouted a warning.

"Stand your ground men, you're breaking the law! Drop your gaff, I'm the water bailiff, Tom Stack, and I want your names! No nonsense now, call out your names!"

In similar situations in the past the shock had been enough to unnerve and petrify the miscreants. Sometimes, they made a dash to escape and in such instances the bailiff, a fit and strapping man, followed one panic-stricken transgressor and generally succeeded in getting the information necessary for a prosecution.

On this occasion, it was different. The night was pitch dark and Tom Stack's torch showed a poor light. When he called on the poachers to provide their names the man with the carbide lamp almost dropped it with shock but the guy with the gaff grabbed the lamp and shone it straight towards the bailiff.

"Cripes, man, if ye take another step," he yelled, "ye're dead!"

The bailiff raised his lamp and shuffled slightly forward, shouting orders and threats that rended the eerie loneliness above the rhythmical sound of lapping water.

"If you don't turn that lamp around and fuck off ye're dead. We'll drown ye in the hole! Move now this minute, now!" the poacher yelled, advancing towards the bailiff. All the time he kept the lamp directed towards him while the poachers were invisible in the dark behind the rim of light.

The bailiff turned the poor light of his torch sideways towards the river and paused. His thoughts raced fast and furiously. He was trying to do an extremely difficult job as best he could. But he was in a lonely and dangerous place, on a pitch black night and faced with a gang of unscrupulous and desperate men. There was no doubt whatsoever in his mind that if he tried to identify them they would harm him. His life was at risk. As they moved slowly towards him he backed away, almost blinded with the strong light. The poachers stood their ground.

"Turn around and beat it! Stay on the bank all the way to the road," the spokesman ordered, "and keep yer torch movin' around so we can see where ye're goin'. One false step an' ye're a goner."

The bailiff went silent, hesitated for some moments, then did as he was ordered. Discretion left no room for valour! When he had disappeared in the distance the poachers struck for home with extreme urgency in the opposite direction.

Next morning there were policemen outside the church gates for masses in Geblik and neighbouring parishes. It was not clear to mass goers what exactly they were looking for but the poachers had been warned by friends who attended an early service and did not go to any church that morning.

"I have an idea," Tom Stack told the police, "that it was that playboy, Pontius Pilate, was the ringleader. I couldn't swear to it, though."

And so the matter was dropped. But the name headed the list of suspected serious poachers to be carefully watched from that point onwards.

*

It was the last week in November 1935 and the salmon were up. Spawning beds brightened the river bottoms. According to reports it was the best run of fish for years. At the same time, unemployment was rife and money was scarce. Pontius Pilate was in dire straits and pushed almost to the limit of his wits for subsistence. He happened to meet with Alice Crosby, the wife of Michael Crosby, a small farmer cum tangler and blocker who lived in a large, plain, two-storey house overlooking Carnalstown Bridge. While he was walking down the village she seemed to go somewhat out of her way to encounter him.

"Would ye be able to make use of a fish?" he enquired.

"In troth, then, I would. Who is it that wouldn't?" she replied.

"I'll tell ye what, then," he told her, his voice lowered somewhat, although there were only a few people around and nobody within hearing distance. "I'm goin' out on Sunday an' I expect I'll be able to help ye. Have the pan ready for taytime. I'll be startin' at the bridge here around twelve o'clock an' I'll call to ye on the way back."

"The blessing of God on you, son," she replied. "You should have a chat with Michael, though. He was talking about you only yesterday. I think he may have a small job in mind for you."

"Begod, then, if that's the case I'll go outta me way to see 'im."

He didn't tell her that he had been drinking with Michael a couple of nights previously because he knew Alice was much opposed to her husband's drinking habits. And she didn't make known to him that she was aware of the session and all the circumstances surrounding it.

Pontius had worked sporadically for Michael Crosby and it was not unusual for them to have a few drinks together now and again. In his own way, Michael was as cash-starved as Pontius, and he too had to organise the odd ruse to cater for particular exigencies. He seldom missed an opportunity to take advantage of circumstances and, if these were slow to arise, he was capable of inventing his own breaks. Where situations tended to be particularly difficult or desperate his wife, Alice, took charge. She was never known to fail.

Tom Stack lived in an adjoining parish and the district he supervised as a water bailiff was extensive, including several parishes. As proof of his diligence he had an attendance book provided by his employers and this was signed daily by someone he might meet in any particular area. Whenever he was in the Carnalstown region he routinely called on Michael Crosby to certify his surveillance and generally he was invited into the house for a mug of tea. Because of such obvious affinity there were those who strongly suspected that Michael got favours for useful inside information supplied to the bailiff. One poacher who was captured, as well as a few others who narrowly escaped, were positive that their misfortune emanated exclusively from this liaison.

Carnalstown Bridge, on the edge of the village, was a landmark with a chequered history. A focal meeting place, it was blown up during the Troubles and when the local IRA men were released from internment and returned triumphantly they were met at the bridge with music and festivities. But the damage to the bridge included a gap of over twenty feet in the road. One of the returning heroes, Joe Shaffrey, was somewhat inebriated and excited on the occasion and decided it would be beneath the dignity of an exultant revolutionary to avail of the menial makeshift gangway. He threw off his coat, rolled up his sleeves and set himself to jump the gap which was about forty foot over the river.

"Don't, Joe, for God's sake, don't jump it," his wife pleaded. "Don't, Joe, don't!"

"Come on, Joe, no bother to ye," one of his sceptical admirers urged, chiding the theatrical bravado. But in the long run he was led like a lamb along the sagging, temporary wooden platform by his overwhelmed wife.

On this November Sunday there were two pairs of intense eyes peering from the spruced-up barn beside Crosby's house and set towards the bridge from midday. There was no sign of Pontius until about half-past-twelve when he suddenly appeared walking spiritedly down the hill above the bridge. He had a long pole on his shoulder and over it a sack was tied at the bottom around which he held a hand. The gaff was unmistakable, although the hook was not visible.

"I'll give him a good lead and then take after him," Tom Stack said edgily to Michael Crosby.

They watched Pontius as he came closer to the bridge wall and wondered which way he would turn. On the downward side of the river about a quarter-mile distant was Hal's Hole, and over a mile further there was a wide, lazy stretch at the river meadow. In between there were placid deep, dark pools and rippling, silvery shallows, with dozens of extensive spawning beds. Ned's Hole, about half a mile away, was on the upward side, where the spawning beds were equally widespread for another mile.

"He'll go for Ned's Hole," Michael Crosby predicted.

He was wrong. Pontius gazed across the parapet on that side but then crossed the road, climbed down the steps and set off on the riverbank towards Hal's Hole. Tom Stack watched until he was almost out of view, then moved deftly through the door, walked smartly out on the road and over the bridge to the steps, and proceeded to shadow Pontius along the river. There was a moment when it seemed the bailiff's plans might be thwarted. As he moved away some distance from the stile and along the bank a shrill whistle pierced the silence. It obviously unnerved Pontius because he went down hunched on one knee for several minutes and glanced furtively around. Then he stood up, gazed intently about him, pulled the cap backways on his head and continued his patrol along the bank.

Tom Stack could allow his quarry to go several hundred yards ahead and still note his exact location – the long handle of the gaff held at an obtuse angle above Pontius Pilate's shoulder betrayed his exact bearing. Without this fortunate telltale pinpoint it would have been very difficult for the bailiff to keep his man under observation, except by moving closer and thereby almost certainly blowing his cover.

The bailiff could have apprehended Pontius at any point along the river. To be caught in such a position during the spawning season, with a gaff, would be sufficient evidence for any court to convict. But the bailiff was determined to ride with his extraordinary good luck – to catch the most wanted poacher around in the act of gaffing a salmon. He was in a no-lose situation: if this failed he could institute proceedings for being in possession of a gaff to illegally appropriate salmon.

Pontius Pilate walked slowly along the river. He peered into spawning beds and noted the copious fish. On occasions he was intrigued by enormous, red-streaked, fighting cock salmon or motionless hens. Sometimes, it was necessary to move away from the riverbank to cross a wide drain or to traverse a particularly difficult fence. He paused or slowed to deliberate on some of the common sights: rabbits and hares scampering or scurrying around; startled water fowl skimming the surface of the river in flight; two swans majestically floating on a deep pool; a flock of ducks noisily flapping downstream; clusters of crested-headed plovers picking and wagging their tails outfield in the raggedly grazed grasses; a dead salmon on the bank whose life had been relinquished to provide one tasty morsel for a marauding otter; cattle and sheep in the pastures; birds in the bushes and flying in the skies. An hour passed by. Then another. Patience was an essential prerequisite for success where the bailiff was concerned and time was not important. He knew he'd got a break that he could hardly have dreamt about. Everything was coming into place and he was playing his cards like a true professional. He had a personal reason to get even with Pontius Pilate. Above all, the publicity resulting from his coup would strike terror into all poachers and identify him as a bailiff to be feared and respected. Pontius kept walking towards his destination and, however long it might take to reach it, Tom Stack was prepared to follow.

*

Pontius was now nearing the spawning beds beside the wooden bridge that linked the Skay Curry with the river meadow. Cattle that had been nibbling the skimpy grasses bucked around apprehensively at his approach, then stood tautly staring with distended eyes and exhaling nostrils. Pontius gave them time to settle and then moved away from the river along a drain to an arched *ceis* with bushes on either side. Beyond this small stone bridge the drain branched in two, so that from above the *ceis* the drain forked to the river.

Tom Stack watched at a distance under cover of furze and bushes. He could identify Pontius retrieving a concealed bucket and spade, taking off his coat and working furiously. There was then the sound of splashing water, followed later by twirling silvery streaks flying through the air. The bailiff decided to interrupt, and moved smartly in on the scene to find an electrified Pontius firing monstrous silver-bellied eels out on the bank. He was so preoccupied with his frantic endeavours that it was more than a minute before he noticed the bailiff standing above him on the *ceis*.

"Cripes, man, is it yerself that's in it? Tom, ye couldn't have come at a better time," he called out without abating his efforts. "Give me a hand wit' these."

Though confused, Tom Stack comprehended the situation at a glance. He noted that the long-handled implement Pontius had been carrying was a drag, not a gaff. The drag was a perfectly legitimate tool with a head like a garden fork but turned at a right angle. It was in common use for cleaning drains and rivers by a man standing on the bank, to pull out weeds and spoilage. In this instance, the handle was more than twice as long as normally used, but its purpose as a lure, to pinpoint deliberately Pontius Pilate's exact location throughout what was an outrageous baiting, registered instantly with the bailiff.

Catching eels in this way was an exercise regularly carried out by Pontius and there was nothing illegal about it. The eels normally crawled unnoticed in the muddy bottoms of drains and had a preference for placid or stagnant stretches, particularly where there was shelter from vegetation, overhanging trees and bushes or bridges. A dead animal thrown into the drain would attract them to a particular location. The operation involved damning the drain on both sides of a *ceis* or bridge and teaming out the water underneath with a scoop or bucket. When the water was emptied out the eels were exposed on the bottom and it was a matter of grabbing one at a time and firing it far out on the bank. As they could crawl at an amazingly fast pace it required considerable alertness to get out in time to secure the catch in a sack, particularly when the eels were large or big numbers were involved. Otherwise, they could escape back into the drain. In this instance, there was a considerable number of large eels. The bailiff was in a state of near shock with the adverse turn his mission had taken. He was speechless.

"Here, hold the sack," Pontius entreated, and Tom Stack found himself holding the bag aloft as the fish were thrown in. Then, when all the eels were secured and the feverish activity and excitement subsided, Pontius put on his coat and sat calmly on a large stone by the *ceis* to smoke a Woodbine.

"Ye'd wonder is it worth it at all," he mused philosophically. "There must be handier ways of spending purgatory."

"It's not an easy way of catching a few lousy eels, all right," Tom Stack replied stiffly.

Light was beginning to dim and crows were flying home to roost. Tom Stack moved sheepishly to leave the scene and had passed over the *ceis* when Pontius called after him.

"Tom, you'll be goin' back to Carnalstown, could I ask ye to do me a favour?"

"What is it?" Tom asked gruffly.

"Ye know the Crosbys, Michael and Alice?"

"Of course I know the Crosbys."

"Well I promised Alice I'd get a fish for her today. Would ye ever mind leaving this bag in with her?"

Pontius held out another sack into which he had transferred a few of the eels. The brazen request galled Tom Stack. He had been outsmarted and humiliated enough already.

"If ye could see yer way to oblige me I'd take the short cut home," Pontius explained, pointing towards the *Geata Gama*.

Tom moved back towards the *ceis* and grimaced quizzically.

"Did ye tell the woman ye'd have an eel for her?"

Pontius appeared nonplussed at the question.

"Cripes, man, I did not! I promised her a fish all right. But doesn't she know it's not the season for trout an' she hardly expected a salmon. Christ, Tom, ye know yerself, ye could get six months for catchin' a salmon. No man in his right mind would chance that! No, Tom, no man would take that chance, not when you're around anyway, doin' the job ye're paid to do. Fair play to ye, Tom, there won't be many salmon taken out of the river when you're around. Ay, no, no, the Crosbys are dacent souls an' they wouldn't encourage anyone to do something wrong."

With that Pontius held out the sack quivering with the jerking eels. Tom took it with little grace and threw it across his shoulder. He had been hoodwinked by a superb professional, and to take a stand on a matter of such little import seemed simply grudging when his real concern was to find out the purpose for the masterly decoy. His instinct told him the sinister reason but he tried to subdue the picture as he retraced the journey with heavy steps, darkness falling all around him.

*

"My advice to ye," Michael Crosby told a distraught bailiff, "is to go home an' keep it to yerself. What can the guards do? Any salmon they got is gone, God only knows where they could be by now. But ye're right, ye were only gone when strange men moved up the other side towards Ned's Hole and don't ye know well they got a few fish. If ye start a rumpus, though, and get the guards ye're only goin' to show yerself up, an' the fool that was made of ye. Take my advice, play it cool and find out whatever ye can tomorrow in broad daylight."

It was wise counsel and Tom Stack abided by it. To go to the police at that stage, in the darkness of the evening, would only start a futile commotion and highlight the hoax, bringing ridicule and unfavourable publicity. Even his competence would be brought into question.

Alice Crosby seethed at the deception. Her concern for the bailiff was palpable.

"The nerve of some people!" she fumed, as she presented him with a hot mug of strong punch to settle his nerves.

On the following Monday morning, Tom Stack was early on the scene and traversed the river from Carnalstown Bridge to Ned's Hole and beyond. He was shocked at his discovery. Every salmon had been poached and not a single fish was left. It was obvious that the river had been dragged expertly with a net and that the logistics involved were beyond the capacity of the common local poacher.

But despite desperate efforts, aided covertly by Michael Crosby, who co-operatively signed his attendance dockets for both days, he could get no useful information regarding the massive poaching. Clearly Pontius Pilate was a vital link in the encircling chain and Tom Stack played fool in the middle.

A few people thought they saw something unusual going on near the river, others heard rumours. What puzzled Tom Stack completely was that to transport safely and promptly the huge catch resulting from such an elaborate scam would involve at least one motorised means of conveyance. In this quiet rural area any vehicle, particularly a strange one, could not but be noted. Yet despite widespread enquiries nobody was located who actually saw anything suspicious. As Micksheen the Blackguard pronounced, there was no Carey in the place, no one saw nothin'. So as the days passed it seemed certain that, barring a miracle, the transgression would remain unsolved.

A further serious difficulty arose for Tom Stack. Some days later, Pontius Pilate called to his house and accused him to his face of crookedness. Abject, obnoxious crookedness.

"I took ye for a dacent, honest man and gave ye four eels to deliver to Alice Crosby. But she only got three. If ye had to ask me for the lot ye could have them. It never dawned on me that ye couldn't be trusted. Cripes, man, I'd take two pins an' report ye!"

The bailiff was devastated. This, on top of what went on before. He had delivered the bag of eels exactly as he received it. And he was certain Pontius knew there was no deliberate interference with it. But it was one man's word against another, and the circumstances under which he had allowed himself to be trapped, if publicised, could undermine his job. He was in a quandary. To go down the road of trying to disprove the accusation, to investigate whether or not he had carelessly lost a fish in transit, would only broadcast his embarrassment.

Pontius did not pursue the matter. It suited his purpose better that way.

"Take my advice," he said cryptically, "an' look after yerself in future. Don't be too hard on a respectable poacher or yer job could be on the line."

Tom Stack understood the menacing meaning, the rate set for his co-operation. He concluded that he was in no position to cavil at the price. At around the same time Pontius called to Colonel Harrington's house. The honourable gentleman had departed to spend the Christmas abroad but left an envelope with his housekeeper for collection. As a consequence Pontius Pilate would have a substantive Christmas as well.

*

The two men in a corner of the pub in Carnalstown were enjoying a quiet drink and deliberating on events of over a week ago.

"Once I heard yer whistle I knew things were goin' right," Pontius Pilate declared. "I told ye not to whistle until he was well out from the bridge so that I could catch sight of 'im with the corner of me eye. After that it was plain sailin'. I kept the handle as high as I could all the time so that he had no trouble seein' it, an' I spotted him through hedges all the way. He thought I was makin' for the spawnin' beds at the river meadow because it's the only spot with a low bank on that side fit for gaffin'. I had things fairly well set up to get th'eels. Mind you, it took Tom Stack longer than I thought to cop on. When he realised what I was at, and that there was no gaff, the bottom fell out of 'im!"

"Ye played yer part bloody well, no doubt about it," his companion admitted. "Ye took the last minute out of it. An' it was all wanted."

"Well, your part was the hardest an' begod it was well done! Ye can't bate good plannin'. The only thing that worried me, though, was where were ye goin' to put the hape o' salmon safely until they were taken away? That was some job."

"No, that was no problem at all," Michael Crosby replied. "We piled them in the barn at the side of the house, an' before midnight they were safely on the road to Dublin!"

Michael was in a very cheerful and outgoing mood on the occasion because, thanks to a job well done and compliments of Colonel Harrington, he too could look forward to an enjoyable Christmas.

"Here, have wan more drink before ye go," Michael entreated.

He was needlessly shouldering an open door because Pontius was incredibly accommodating in that regard. In fact, there was time for many more rounds before the pub was emptied. Conversation meantime ranged from the trite to the profoundly philosophical.

"There's a thing," Pontius blurted, in his manner of introducing a fresh subject, and wiping the froth of the pint of Guinness from his mouth, "I often be thinkin' that fish is very peculiar."

Michael Crosby took time to consider the grave assertion.

"There's no doubt about it," he agreed. "Fish is the peculiarist thing ye could think of. If fish could live outta water where would the like of us fit in?"

Then Pontius was called on to sing, and after the stirring strains of *Kevin Barry* and *Boolavogue*, the animated Irishmen set for home with patriotic spirits and porter pumping in their veins.

*

It was a couple of days before Christmas and Alice Crosby was putting some final touches to the kitchen for the festive season. In the mid-afternoon she was on her knees scrubbing a corner of the floor, with her face to the wall, when she was startled to find Tom Stack standing in the room beside her. He held a bag in his hand.

"It's only a small salmon," he explained, proffering it to her as she rose to her feet, untying the strings of a smudgy apron. "I knew you were upset over that blackguard, Pontius Pilate, and the villainy he caused. This is the best I could do for you to make up for the disappointment."

"Ah, Tom, you shouldn't!" she reproached him appreciatively. "My God, after all you went through, to be thinking of me! How on earth did you manage it?"

"Well," the bailiff replied, "I have to show appreciation for all the times Michael signed the attendance dockets for me, sometimes backdating for weeks. And you needn't worry about the fish – there's nothing crooked about it. I got it from a reliable source, a friend of Colonel Harrington. The Colonel is a good friend of mine and, like Michael, signs the dockets for me when I'm in that end of the district. He's on holidays abroad at the moment but he'll sign for me when he comes back."

"Just so," Alice commented with a resolute sideways nod of the head that betokened understanding and appreciation.

She seated him at the table and set about preparing a mug of punch, thanking him profusely all the time. In the middle of it all Michael walked in the door and also expressed gratitude and wonder at the very acceptable present. A steaming mug of punch was placed on the table for him as well.

"I hope ye got over the terrible nightmare," he declared with deep concern after a satisfying slug of the hot beverage.

"I haven't, Michael, to tell the truth. Will I ever get over it? But I'm tryin' to do the best I can. I learned a few hard lessons I won't forget in a hurry, I can tell ye."

"The way the world is going, Tom, you wouldn't know who you could trust," Alice opined. "Honest to God, there's rogues around and you wouldn't think butter'd melt in their mouths."

"She's right, Tom, she's right," Michael agreed. "Ye can't take nobody for granted nowadays. There's people playin' up to yer face an' watchin' to stab ye in the back."

Talk and banter continued for another half an hour. When the bailiff finally rose to go Michael directed a personal question at him.

"There's a thing, Tom, d'ye ever have a talla?"

"Well, I don't, Michael. I never had one since I took up this job. Ye can only get one from constant pullin' – weedin', milkin' gibbin' cocks o'hay an' the like."

"The reason I'm askin' is that we have the skins of th'eels that Pontius Pilate got ye to take to us. An' an eel skin wrapped around the wrist is th'only cure for a talla."

"Begod you're right," Tom confessed. "And from time to time I meet lots of fellas that can't tie their boots with tallas."

"Here," said Michael, "take them wit' ye and ye'll be able to help somebody in yer travels. They're all in that," and he handed a packet to the bailiff who collected his bicycle at the gate and presently cycled out of sight.

When he reached home, Tom Stack went to a small shed at the rear of the house and opened the packet to shelve the contents. In it he found four eel skins.

*

Description of the details connected with the poaching stroke did not take long. "Water under the bridge," Michael Crosby commented. "A job of successful teamwork. To think that nearly half a mile of spawning beds were stripped of salmon starting at the village edge, without being noticed by a single individual, was a feat that could hardly ever be repeated. My problem is to give honour where it is due. Who most deserves credit for the success of the mission?"

The number directly involved was small – Pontius Pilate, Michael and Alice Crosby and Colonel Harrington. Without the input from each the job would not have been possible. But the input of Alice Crosby was critically significant, having regard to all the factors. And it was she who handled the question in the end.

"Let's come to a decision now," she said. "There will be bad times ahead requiring the same kind of organising. We'll wait for a few more runs to agree on some conclusions."

A sensible proposition from an incomparable schemer, Pontius Pilate allowed. It would probably have helped him in his conclusions if he had known that Alice Crosby worked in the summer for nearly two months as a housekeeper with Colonel Harrington. And she never missed an opportunity to scheme for better days. But as she claimed herself – what you don't know won't sicken you.

The White Plague

Carnalstown was a small nondescript village on the southern end of the parish of Geblik and nothing of consequence ever happened there. But things were different on the last Sunday of September, 1947, and there was palpable excitement throughout the area. The main reason for the stir was that, at three o'clock on that day, the village team of Carnalstown was due to play the final for the Ruhan Cup. This, in fact, would be a replay, as the original game, under GAA rules, was played around four months previously and the result was unsatisfactory – among other consequences it ended in a draw.

The standard of football was quite high as the participating teams all belonged to senior ranks, with the exception of Carnalstown who were intermediate champions and played quality football.

When the original game was played there had been great, in fact unreasonable, expectations that Oweny Caffrey would succeed in getting promoted to the county senior team. Elderly men used their imagination to predict the play that would take place between Oweny and Buller Hogan, who played on the 40 yards for Garstown.

Buller is getting on, some said, and Oweny Caffrey will hold him. Others went further – Oweny Caffrey would hold him the best day ever he was. He won't get a ball, much less a score.

It turned out differently. On the day, Buller got every ball and beat the team almost on his own. Oweny Caffrey tried. But he had no pace, no energy, no breath. The followers were at first aghast, then impatient, then cruel.

"The fecker's afraid of Buller Hogan!"

"A holy show!"

"Never had guts, only a big bully like all the Caffreys, cowards when it was put up to them!"

Before half-time a high ball came down that he should have caught easily but it went through his hands.

"Why didn't you bring a sack," someone yelled, and the Garstown followers roared approval. He was taken off then amid boos and yells from the same people who had cheered him off the pitch in the past and, in fact, not so very long ago.

"People have very short memories," said the Kithen, an old man who was noted for his wisdom. "I'd love to think it was Buller Hogan that has improved, but I'm afraid."

In the weeks that followed Oweny Caffrey was the subject of many a hushed conversation. "What do you think of him? Didn't he get damnable shook? Ah, I'm afraid, I'm afraid..."

Oweny knew that people's eyes were constantly on him. Many avoided him. On one occasion he was speaking to a woman who was a friend of the family at the gateway to her house and her three children came close beside her. "Will yous go to hell outta that and not be gawking into the man's face," she cautioned them.

But Oweny knew it was not the inquisitiveness that upset her, but the danger. Consumption was the death penalty and it was highly contagious. It was known as the white plague.

Over the months before that football match, Oweny Caffrey had felt his health deserting him. He had gone to see different doctors but they all told him the same story. One of them had told him that his problem was in the mind, to go home and buy a skipping rope to exercise himself.

On the day after the match he went to another doctor, who still could find nothing wrong but sent him for an x-ray. When the result came back, the doctor delivered it in positive terms. "Your right lung is perfect," he said.

The left lung was the problem. Within days he was in the TB block of the county hospital. It was a large ward on the first floor – the ground floor was packed with blankets from the beginning of the war, in times of the Emergency. The female ward was its duplicate on the left-hand side of the stairs. None of the patients was allowed outside the very restrictive bounds without permission. They could not go near the main hospital at the front. Towards the rear there was a high wall surrounding the yard. Here there were four open wooden huts in which four male patients with consumptive sores lay on their backs night and day. One of these patients was a pal of Oweny Caffrey – they had played football together. The first time Oweny visited the hut and saw the sore on the man's back he almost fainted.

"You could push your fist into it," he told friends afterwards.

Even for visitors, the TB block was a depressing conjunct. There was a feeling of dreariness and despair. Some patients lay in their beds, others sat disconsolately in chairs. Always, there were some walking around, feebly and nervous, going nowhere or for no purpose. All the time there was raking coughing and an atmosphere of despair. The nights were the worst. At the start, Oweny was shaken. In the early night of his third day, Nurse Murray told him not to be shocked if the patient in the fifth bed from him died during the night. When he wakened up later in the night, a rosary for the dying was being said but it was for the patient in the bed beside him. As time passed, death became commonplace and it wasn't always those who looked the worst that died. No wonder children were not allowed to visit the place.

During the next three months, Oweny paid two visits to Peamount Sanatorium to check his suitability for treatment there, his only hope. Food in the TB block of the hospital was very good but in Peamount, contrary to expectations, it was very poor. Turnips sliced, with a burnt rasher for dinner. But those that could afford to pay for food were allowed to purchase it and consume it.

In Peamount, the men were on one side and the women on the other. In the TB block of the county hospital, patients were watching every week for an announcement that they would get to Peamount. This was the only hope for survival. Oweny complained about the food in Peamount – there were flies, insects and snails in the cabbage and turnips, three of them in one day. Oweny expressed the view that the food they were given to eat would not be consumed by Ballymaquinn Monarch, but of course the medical practitioner was unaware that this dog was a famous Kerry greyhound at the time. Most of the inmates were old and there to die. People thought at the time that going to Peamount was the end, but in fact it was the opposite. And, of course, the magical word was streptomycin, associated with the medical man and politician by the name of Dr Noel Browne. One man who was in a position to pay for streptomycin was allowed to use the drug and was cured.

*

Against that background it was only natural that Oweny Caffrey would be seriously upset if he could not attend the match. The football grounds were just across the road from the hospital and

Oweny had his heart set on watching the game. He was located at the rear of the TB block and had been there for nearly four months now. Seven other of the male patients planned to go to the game if they felt well enough on the day. On the Friday, Nurse Murray had given permission to all of them, with one exception – Oweny Caffrey.

"She has a knife in me," he declared to anyone who cared to listen. Tom, the burly wardsman, had a particular interest in developments. He came from the same rural parish as Oweny Caffrey and he knew the family well.

"As thick as a double-ditch, every one of them. Decent alright, I'll grant you that. But horrible round. She'll have to change her mind and let him go to the match, otherwise Oweny says home he'll go."

"He's not that big an eejit," Dick, the receptionist in the hospital, protested.

"I'm tellin' you he is," Tom insisted. "That's the type of the Caffreys – the heart of the rowl but stubborn as mules! I saw Nurse Murray tame the likes of him many a time before."

"Here, then," he challenged. "I'll bet a pound I'm right. If Oweny doesn't get to the match, he'll go home."

"Done with you," agreed Dick.

So the substantial bet was made. Word spread to other members of the staff and there was a sense of excitement as all covertly watched Oweny's moves. Three o'clock would be the moment of truth, as soon as Nurse Murray arrived to inspect the ward. At two o'clock, a feeling of delight and satisfaction came over Tom as he noticed Oweny Caffrey gathering the few belongings in his locker into a bag.

"Don't tell me you're thinking of leaving," he asked with mock concern.

"By God I am," Oweny retorted. "She'll not walk on me any longer. I'm the only one in this place that she's down on, night, noon and morning. All the time it's 'Caffrey, did I not tell you this?' or 'did I not tell you that?' I'm taking no more of it. If I'm not allowed out for the match, I'm going home."

"You're dead right," Tom encouraged him. "If there's one thing I can't stand it's picking on someone for nothing. And it's going to be a great game, everyone tells me. I wouldn't take it myself, I can tell you."

And so the stage was set for a showdown, where it did not seem possible that anyone could be a winner.

*

Wardsman Tom took a particular note of the proceedings. At a quarter to three, Oweny Caffrey walked towards the door of the male ward with his case and some small parcels. He left them inside the door of the ward where they were in full view of the nurse, who sat at a desk in the opposite corner.

Not a word was spoken between Oweny Caffrey and Nurse Murray. In about another ten seconds Oweny would be on his way out of the hospital. But just as he approached his case and parcels, Nurse Murray flicked a finger at him. Reluctantly, he went up to meet her at her desk and stared at the floor without saying a word.

"Oweny," Nurse Murray began, in what could be regarded as a sympathetic tone. "I understand your predicament and I trust that you understand mine."

"No, I don't," he retorted loudly.

"The simple matter," continued Oweny Caffrey, "is that seven other male patients have permission to go to the game and you gave that permission to all of them. I was the only exception.

"Not alone that," he continued, "but on every occasion I ask you for a concession you fail to deliver it. In plain language, I am the only one who is victimised."

"Well, let me put it this way," Nurse Murray retorted. "If you have been victimised the fault is not mine."

"How do you mean the fault is not yours? Of course the fault is yours. It couldn't be anyone else's."

"The situation facing me is this – seven other TB patients have requested permission to go to the match and that permission has been given. Yours is the only one that has been refused. But the reality of the situation is that not one of these seven patients has a chance of getting cured or home from hospital. You are the only one that has been assessed with a hope of survival. The prospects are not great in your case, either."

Oweny Caffrey straightened himself up slowly with a slight feeling of pleasure which he had not experienced for a long time. There was a lengthy and awkward period of silence.

"Thank you, Matron," he said with feeling, shuffling nervously all the time. He gathered up his belongings and took them back to the locker at the side of his bed. Later, wardsman Tom put the question to him: "Did you lose your nerve, or what, Oweny? It wouldn't be like a Caffrey to lose his cool."

"Well", Oweny replied with a sense of candour and elation, "Nurse Murray made a point that stumped me. The decision was simply taken out of my hands."

Release From Hell Of A Parish

Sorrows and troubles are interminably intertwined. For a few years after Very Rev. JL Convey was appointed parish priest of Geblik in the mid-1940s, he endured a surfeit of both afflictions. Firstly, his right-hand assistant for parochial duties, Marcus Clerkin, fathered a child with a local farmer's daughter and they would have to get married at the side altar. Fr Convey agreed to marry them at seven o'clock in the morning when there would be no other parishioners present. He made this arrangement to avoid causing scandal and embarrassment for the respected families. Instead it had the opposite effect; complaints reached his ears that there was one law for the rich and another for the poor.

A second unfortunate incident also related to the marriage of a young farmer and farmer's daughter, both from very highly regarded families. Fr Convey asked them was there any impediment to the marriage, basically meaning was the girl pregnant, in which case the ceremony would have to take place at the side altar. They assured him there was none so the proceedings had all the trappings of a royal wedding as regards numbers, style, presents and entertainment. It was a cause, then, of deep anguish for Fr Convey when a baby was born within six months of the marriage. But these afflictions, although deeply troubling for the good priest, were trifling compared to the virtual hell he was destined to endure.

Matt Kenny was a roadworker in the parish. He and his wife Lena lived in a small cottage with a large family, undisciplined and wild. The eldest daughter had a baby outside marriage and emigrated to England. According to reports, she was doing well there. The boys were affable but mischievously inclined and most of them also emigrated to England. In 1947, a daughter, Kathleen, nicknamed Kitser, was the eldest remaining. She was very bossy and domineering and, although not noticeable, there were rumours she was pregnant.

Séamus Fitzhenry lived within half a mile of the Kennys. His father, Jamesy, was a farm labourer living in poor circumstances but, through the interest of the parish priest Séamus was attending secondary school in Skell, which was run by the Christian Brothers. He cycled the eight-mile journey every day and, despite inclement weather and continual bicycle problems, his attendance record was good. For a period of eight weeks he had to resort to Shank's mare as the tyres on his bicycle were worn out and replacements could not be afforded at the high black-market prices. The problem was sorted out when the Brother Superior arranged with a sympathetic garage owner to supply two tyres at the recommended retail price of five shillings, ten pence each.

At school in Skell, Séamus was always addressed by his proper name but in Geblik it was invariably Pilate, and usually Young Pilate. Of course, he regarded the distinction as intentionally degrading but there was nothing he could do about it. He passed the intermediate certificate examination with honours and was set to prepare for the leaving certificate. On the first week after the holidays, however, he fell ill and had to rest at home. He recovered somewhat in a few days, and on the Friday decided to go for a walk and meet a few people. His first call was to the

Kennys' cottage.

Kitser was busy with household chores. Her mother, Lena, frail and gaunt, was seated at the fire but left to go to bed within minutes of his entry. After a while spent discussing inconsequential affairs, Kitser lay down on a bench attached to a partition fronting the fire. Her dress was pulled up above the waist exposing her bum. What Séamus found intriguing was the style and artistry of her underwear – a thick black cloth sewn with white thread, faultlessly and impeccably executed. It was evident that Kitser would be incapable of producing any garment to such a high standard.

It was also clear to Séamus that Kitser was tempting him to indulge in sex. He had no doubt that he was constrained by the Sixth Commandment but the occasion somewhat excited him.

"I have no water to make a cup of tea, will you take me a bucket from the pump?" Kitser asked.

The roadside pump was only a short distance away but Séamus was aware that old Jimmy Murtagh spent most of his time on a seat at the pump and he would recognise Kitser's bucket. So he showed no inclination to oblige.

"Now, Pilate," Kitser advised, "don't look a gift horse in the mouth. If you get me a bucket of water I'll give you half an hour in the bed."

Whether swayed by strength, weakness or divine grace, Séamus resisted the temptation and left with discomfiting feelings of inadequacy.

*

Fr Convey was riding a big white horse along the road from the village and he stopped outside the Kenny cottage. As the horse pranced impatiently the priest called in a loud voice across the fence.

"Kathleen? Are you there, Kathleen?"

Kitser had noted his approach and came out the door immediately.

"Who is the father of this child?" the priest demanded.

Without hesitation, Kitser responded: "Widower Rally."

Fr Convey immediately turned the horse around and departed at a trot up the gravelled side road in the direction of Jack Rally's cottage, less than a mile away.

*

Autumn had arrived and the good weather continued. Séamus Fitzhenry had worked all summer on the bog, missing school and the opportunity to complete the first year of the two-year leaving certificate course. He was dismayed at the plight, but poverty allows for no concessions. He was now engaged on his last job on the bog. His father had cut and harvested a big crop of turf for a merchant in Skell who wanted to have it delivered. It was in clamps on the bank and involved considerable work. All the organisation was through his father, who arranged that Séamus would assist Kitser Kenny with the task. Kitser had an ass and cart and, although pregnant, was a formidable manual worker. The job was really one for strong men, and Séamus wondered if there could be a covert reason for the engagement of Kitser. But he kept those thoughts to himself.

The bog was desolate, not a soul in sight. At lunchtime, the pair took milk and sandwiches, sitting apart behind a clamp of turf. Suddenly, a voice broke the silence.

"God bless the work."

It was widower Jack Rally, who had emerged from a clump of birch. He had an autocycle as a means of transport but obviously left it some distance away so as not to betray his presence. Kitser showed no interest but got up and resumed work. The widower, thwarted in his plans, moved off too. In a short while the sound of an autocycle broke the silence and Séamus contemplated the frustration of a disappointed man.

*

Tom Johnson was a handyman in his early twenties. Responsible and affable, he was seldom out of work. He had an old motorcar which he used to transport friends to and from dances at a small charge. On this particular night, sometime after midnight, he drove into his own yard and parked the car behind the house. As he moved towards the door he was shocked to notice a man walking past him towards the gate. He was too unnerved to follow or to ask any questions, but in the dim light he figured the man was Oweny Murphy, a heavily built, middle-aged bachelor. Next day, he made it his business to confront Oweny Murphy.

"What were you doing in my shed at that hour?" he asked him.

"Ah, don't worry about it," Murphy replied. "I was only having a go at the 'oul ass."

Tom Johnson understood what bestiality meant and he was shocked to have any association with such evil. That night he called to Fr Convey and related his predicament to him.

"What will I do, father?" he pleaded.

The good priest was equally upset.

"Has this ever happened before?" he inquired.

"I don't know," Tom replied, "but I noticed Murphy's old

green van behind a clump of trees near the house and I saw it there several times before."

After a pause, Fr Convey spoke in a low voice.

"Tom," he said, "the next time you spot the van there, let me know straight away."

Tom readily agreed to this request.

Several weeks passed without any developments. Then, more or less by accident one night, Tom spotted the van in the dusk and drove straight down to Fr Convey.

"I'll go back with you in your car," the priest told him.

They drove back and Fr Convey went into the shed with a torch lamp but there were only two animals there, a cow and a donkey. They returned to the parochial house and the priest was seriously upset; he had hoped that by confronting Oweny Murphy on the site of the misdemeanour he would have been able to bring finality to the atrocious scandal. Now he realised that the problem could only be sorted out with God's help in the future and the concern should be to dissuade pernicious gossip.

"Do not discuss this matter with anyone," he pleaded.

Tom assured him in that regard and faithfully kept his promise. But the notoriety of the area, and of the people who lived there, would effectively never recover.

*

Kitser Kenny was in severe pain from before midnight. She realised she was about to give birth to a baby and had made no special provisions for the event, no arrangements for a nurse to be present or for any other assistance. When the baby was delivered it was dead so she got a spade, dug a hole in a secluded corner of the garden and buried it there. Then she went to the cow park about half a mile away, milked the cow and carried home the can of milk. It was Sunday morning, so she dressed in a perfunctory manner and set for mass in Holmogats.

In the small church she sat alone at the window. She was very petulant always, so nobody in the small congregation had the temerity to inquire about her health. By evening, however, she was a patient in the county hospital and at the same time the police began an investigation into the circumstances surrounding the plight of the baby.

In due course she was summoned to appear in court, where the case was heard *in camera*. It was decided that no criminal activity was involved so Kitser was released and, within two months, emigrated to England where she joined her sister who looked after her there. By all accounts she was a transformed woman and never afterwards got into any difficulty.

*

Fr Convey felt the pressures associated with running the parish of Geblik were too much for him and he decided with considerable regret to seek a change of parish. The bishop and he were from the same part of the country and knew each other well. His Lordship was surprised and disappointed at the request but understood the predicament. Within a matter of months diocesan changes were announced and Fr Convey was appointed parish priest of Bohermore, a rural parish like Geblik but somewhat larger.

A short time later there was a *Propagation of the Faith* collection and the amounts of subscriptions by the parishes were published. The curate in Geblik read out the details from the altar. The amount for Bohermore was only slightly higher than for Geblik and the priest emphasised that fact; he was making the obvious point that Fr Convey's transfer could not be regarded as upgrading, which highlighted the sad reality that he did not comprehend the travails and shortcomings of the parish.

Comprehension is a human, not just religious, *sine qua non*; there is no substitute for savvy.

Other books by Jack Fitzsimons

Bungalow Bashing

Bungalow Bliss

By the Banks of the Borora

Call Me a Dreamer and Other Yarns

Coursing Ban Be Damned!

Democracy Be Damned!

New Homes From Old

The Parish Of Kilbeg

Peeping Through The Reeds

The Plains of Royal Meath

Sermons

Thatched Cottages In County Meath

Towards The Emancipation Of Woman